∽ Music Scores ∾

OMNIBUS

Part 1

Earliest Music Through the Works of Beethoven

WILLIAM J. STARR and **GEORGE F. DEVINE**

Department of Fine Arts, University of Tennessee, Knoxville, Tennessee

PRENTICE-HALL INC ENGLEWOOD CLIFFS NEW JERSEY

PRENTICE-HALL INTERNATIONAL, INC.,   *London*
PRENTICE-HALL OF AUSTRALIA, PTY., LTD.,   *Sydney*
PRENTICE-HALL OF CANADA, LTD.,   *Toronto*
PRENTICE-HALL OF INDIA (PRIVATE), LTD.,   *New Delhi*
PRENTICE-HALL OF JAPAN, INC.,   *Tokyo*
PRENTICE-HALL DE MEXICO, S.A.,   *Mexico City*

Second printing.......July, 1964

∽ Preface ∾

. This anthology, of very broad scope, has been brought together as a result of some years' observation of undergraduate needs in music literature and theory courses and is in line with the current trend to provide the student closer contact with actual music. Too often the undergraduate gets only a glimpse of these scores in editions and specialized anthologies belonging to a music department. True, many of the later works that appear here are available in separate scores and collected works, but the editors feel that a significant collection brought together "under one roof" at a reasonable price could be very helpful to both instructors and students. It is hoped that these volumes become an integral part of the student's permanent library.

With an aim toward providing a practical book for undergraduates following a well-trodden path in their studies, the editors have admittedly and deliberately included a host of familiar titles. Many compositions appear in their entirety, and excerpts have enough scope to preserve the character of the composition. Each title illustrates a form, a style, and one or more important compositional devices. A wide spectrum of the various musical media is presented: vocal and instrumental, large and small ensemble.

Practically every musical composition contained herein is readily available on recordings and due to the presentation in open score, many of them can be performed in class.

For convenience and ease of handling, the collection is divided into two volumes. Part I contains examples from earliest music through Beethoven's writings. Part II contains compositions of the Romantic and Impressionistic periods and an excerpt from Stravinsky's transitional *Rite of Spring*.

Details concerning sources of the early music are given in the appendix of Part I. Both available facsimiles and modern editions are listed. Several of the medieval pieces were transcribed from other than the familiar sources. Some examples are adaptations of secondary sources, modernized for ease of performance and reading. The old clefs have been retained in several examples so that the student may gain proficiency in reading them.

It is hoped that this panorama of Western music history will be interesting, informative, and helpful in the development of true musicianship.

W. J. S.
G. F. D.

Contents

Contents (continued)

Contents

Part 2

Skolion of Seikelos

a. Modern notation

Ho - son dzes phai - nou, me - den ho - los sy ly - pou.

Pros o - li - gon es - ti to dzen, to te - los ho chro - nos ap - ai - tei.

b. Greek letter notation

C   Z̄   Z̄   KIZ   Ī   K̄   I   Z   IK   O   C̄   OΦ   C

Ο - σον ζηις φαι νου μη - δὲν ὅ - λως σύ λυ - ποῦ πρὸς

K   Z   I   KI   K   C̄   OΦ   C   K   O   I   Z   K   C   C̄   CXĪ

ὀ - λί - γον ἐσ - τὶ το ζῆν τὸ τέ - λος ὁ χρό - νος ἀπ - αι - τεῖ

Missa in Dominica Resurrectionis

Intr. IV

R e - sur - ré - xi,   * et ad·huc te - cum sum,

al - le - lú - ja: po - su - ís - ti su - per me

ma - num tu - am, al - le - lú - ja: mi - rá - bi - lis

fac - ta est sci - én - ti - a tu - a, al - le - lú - ja,

al - le - lú - ja. Ps. Dó - mi - ne, pro - bás - ti me, et

cog - no - vís - ti me: * tu cog - no - vís - ti ses - si - ó - nem me - am,

et re - sur - rec - ti - ó - nem me - am. Gló - ri - a Pa·tri et Fí - li - o,

1

et Spi-rí-tu-i Sancto. ✱ Sic-ut e-rat in princí-pi-o, et nunc,

et semper, et in sǽ-cu-la sæ-cu-ló-rum. A-men.

VIII

K

ý-ri-e, ✱ e-lé-i-son. *iij.* Chris-te,

e-lé-i-son. *iij.* Ký-ri-e, e-lé-i-son. *ij.*

Ký-ri-e, ✱ e-lé-i-son.

IV

G

ló-ri-a in excél-sis De-o. Et in ter-ra pax

ho-mí-ni-bus bo-næ vo-luntá-tis. Lau-dámus te. Be-ne-dí-

ci-mus te. Ado-rámus te. Glo-ri-fi-cámus te.

Grá-ti-as á-gi-mus ti-bi propter mag-nam gló-ri-am tu-am.

Dó-mi-ne De-us, Rex cæ-lés-tis, De-us Pa-ter omní-po-tens.

Dó-mi-ne Fi-li u-ni-gé-ni-te, Je-su Chris-te. Dó-mi-ne De-us,

Agnus De-i, Fí-li-us Pa-tris. Qui tol-lis pec-cá-ta

mun-di, mi-se-ré-re no-bis. Qui tol-lis peccá-ta mundi,

súsci-pe depre-ca-ti-ó-nem nostram. Qui se-des ad déx-te-ram

Pa-tris, mi-se-ré-re no-bis. Quó-ni-am tu so-lus sanctus.

Tu so-lus Dó-mi-nus. Tu so-lus Al-tís-simus, Je-su Chris-te.

Cum Sancto Spí-ri-tu,   in gló-ri-a De-i   Pa-tris.

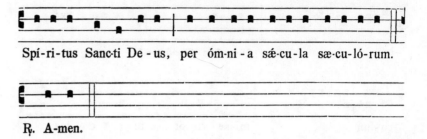

Spí-ri-tus Sanc-ti De-us,   per óm-ni-a sǽ-cu-la sæ-cu-ló-rum.

A   -   men.

℞. A-men.

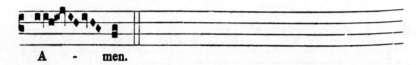

D ó-mi-nus vo-bíscum. ℞. Et cum spí-ri-tu tu-o.   O-rémus.

Léctio Epístolæ beáti Pauli Apóstoli ad Corínthios
1 Cor. 5, 7-8

Fratres: Expurgáte vetus ferméntum, ut sitis nova conspérsio, sicut estis ázymi. Etenim Pascha nostrum immolátus est Christus. Itaque epulémur: non in ferménto véteri, neque in ferménto malítiæ et nequítiæ: sed in ázymis sinceritátis et veritátis.

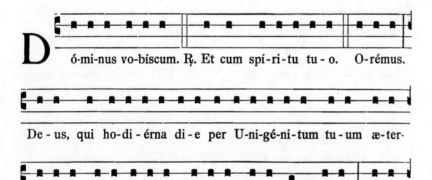

De-us, qui ho-di-érna di-e per U-ni-gé-ni-tum tu-um æ-ter-

ni-tá-tis no-bis ád-i-tum, de-víc-ta mor-te, re-se-rás-ti: vo-ta

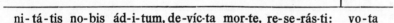

nostra, quæ præ-ve-ni-éndo aspí-ras,   ét-i-am adju-vándo pro-

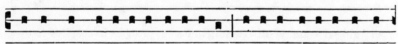

sé-que-re. Per e-ún-dem Dó-mi-num nostrum Je-sum Chris-tum,

Fí-li-um tu-um: Qui te-cum vi-vit et regnat in u-ni-tá-te

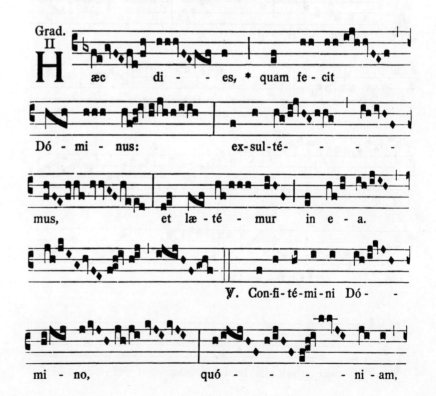

Grad.
II

Hæc di   -   es, * quam fe-cit

Dó - mi - nus: ex-sul-té - -

mus,   et læ-té - mur in e-a.

℣. Con-fi-té-mi-ni Dó - -

mi - no,   quó - - - ni-am,

bo - - nus: quó - ni - am in sǽ - - -

cu-lum   mi-se - ri-cór - di - a * e - jus.

VII

A l-le-lú - ja. * *ij.*

℣. Pascha nos - trum   immo-

lá - - - - - -

tus   est * Chris - tus.

Sequ.
I

V íc-timæ paschá - li laudes * ímmo-lent Chris-ti - á-ni.

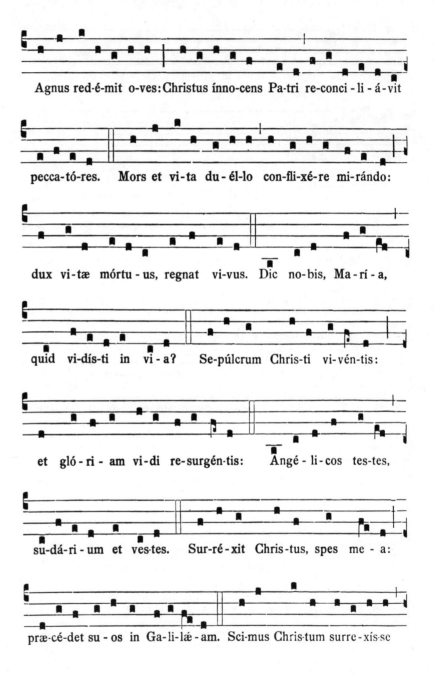

Agnus red-é-mit o-ves: Christus ínno-cens Pa-tri re-conci - li - á-vit

pecca-tó-res.   Mors et vi-ta du - él-lo con-fli-xé-re mi-rándo:

dux vi-tæ mórtu - us, regnat vi-vus. Dic no-bis, Ma - rí - a,

quid vi-dís-ti in vi - a?   Se-púlcrum Chris-ti vi-vén-tis:

et gló - ri - am vi-di re-surgén-tis: Angé - li-cos tes-tes,

su-dá-ri - um et ves-tes.   Sur-ré-xit Chris-tus, spes me - a:

præ-cé-det su - os in Ga-li-lǽ - am. Sci-mus Chris-tum surre-xís-se

a mór·tu - is ve·re: tu no·bis, vic·tor Rex, mi·se·ré - re.

A - men. Al·le·lú · ja.

✠ Sequéntia sancti Evangélii secúndum Marcum
Marc. 16, 1-7

In illo témpore: María Magdaléne, et María Jacóbi, et Salóme emérunt arómata, ut veniéntes úngerent Jesum. Et valde mane una sabbatórum, véniunt ad monuméntum, orto jam sole. Et dicébant ad ínvicem: Quis revólvet nobis lápidem ab óstio monuménti? Et respiciéntes vidérunt revolútum lápidem. Erat quippe magnus valde. Et introeúntes in monuméntum vidérunt júvenem sedéntem in dextris, coopértum stola cándida, et obstupuérunt. Qui dicit illis: Nolíte expavéscere: Jesum quæritis Nazarénum, crucifíxum: surréxit, non est hic, ecce locus, ubi posuérunt eum. Sed ite, dícite discípulis ejus et Petro, quia præcédit vos in Galilæam: ibi eum vidébitis, sicut dixit vobis.

IV

Cre·do in u·num De - um. Patrem omni·po·téntem, factó·rem

cæ·li et terræ, vi·si·bí·li · um ómni · um et in·vi·si·bí·li · um.

Et in u·num Dó·mi·num Je·sum Chris·tum, Fí·li · um De - i

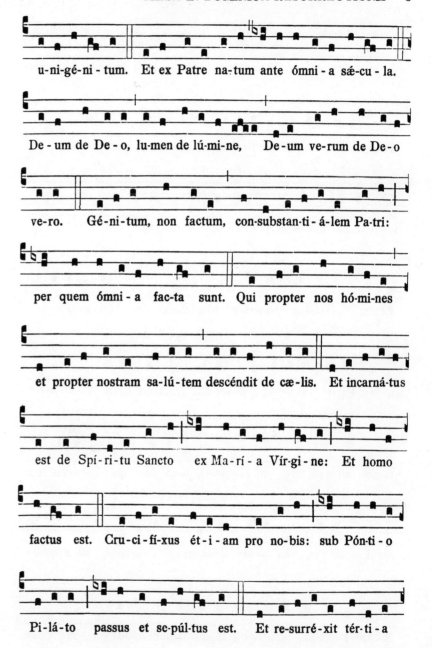

u·ni·gé·ni · tum. Et ex Patre na·tum ante ómni · a sǽ·cu · la.

De - um de De - o, lu·men de lú·mi·ne, De·um ve·rum de De - o

ve·ro. Gé·ni·tum, non factum, con·substan·ti · á·lem Pa·tri:

per quem ómni · a fac·ta sunt. Qui propter nos hó·mi·nes

et propter nostram sa·lú·tem descéndit de cæ·lis. Et incarná·tus

est de Spí·ri·tu Sancto ex Ma·rí · a Vír·gi · ne: Et homo

factus est. Cru·ci·fí·xus ét·i·am pro no·bis: sub Pón·ti · o

Pi·lá·to passus et se·púl·tus est. Et re·surré·xit tér·ti · a

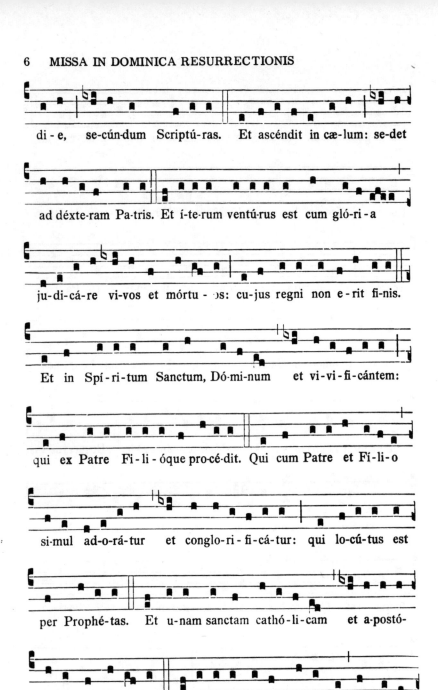

di - e, se-cún-dum Scriptú-ras. Et ascéndit in cæ-lum: se-det

ad déxte-ram Pa-tris. Et í-te-rum ventú-rus est cum gló-ri - a

ju-di-cá-re vi-vos et mórtu - os: cu-jus regni non e - rit fi-nis.

Et in Spí-ri-tum Sanctum, Dó-mi-num et vi-vi-fi-cántem:

qui ex Patre Fi - li - óque pro-cé-dit. Qui cum Patre et Fí-li-o

si-mul ad-o-rá-tur et conglo-ri - fi-cá-tur: qui lo-cú-tus est

per Prophé-tas. Et u-nam sanctam cathó-li-cam et a-postó-

li-cam Ecclé-si - am. Confí-te - or u-num baptís-ma in re-mis-

si - ó-nem pec-ca-tó-rum. Et exspéc-to re-surrec-ti - ó-nem

mortu - ó-rum. Et vi-tam ventú - ri sǽ-cu-li. A - men.

Offert.
IV

Ter - ra * tré-mu - it, et qui - é - vit,

dum re-súrge - ret in ju-dí - ci - o De - us,

al - le - - - lú-ja.

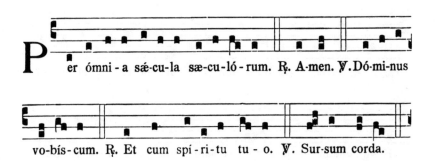

Per ómni - a sǽ-cu-la sæ-cu-ló-rum. ℞. A-men. ℣.Dó-mi-nus

vo-bís-cum. ℞. Et cum spí-ri-tu tu - o. ℣. Sur-sum corda.

℟. Ha-bé-mus ad Dó-mi-num. ℣. Grá-ti - as a-gá-mus Dó-mi-no,

De - o nos-tro. ℟. Dig-num et justum est. Ve-re dignum et

justum est, æquum et sa-lu-tá-re: Te qui-dem, Dó-mi-ne, omni

tém-po-re, sed in hac po-tís-si-mum di - e glo-ri - ó-si - us

præ-di - cá-re, cum Pascha nostrum immo-lá - tus est Chris-tus.

Ipse e-nim ve-rus est Agnus, qui ábstu-lit pec-cá-ta mundi.

Qui mortem nostram mo-ri - éndo destrú-xit et vi - tam re-sur-

géndo re-pa-rá-vit. Et íd-e - o cum Ange-lis et Arch-ánge-lis,

cum Thro-nis et Do-mi-na-ti - ó-ni-bus cum-que omni mi-lí-

ti - a cæ-lés-tis ex-ér-ci-tus hymnum gló-ri-æ tu - æ cá-ni-mus,

si - ne fi - ne di-céntes:

IV
Sanctus, * Sanctus, Sanctus Dó-mi-nus, De - us Sá-ba - oth.

Ple - ni sunt cæ - li et terra gló - ri - a tu - a. Ho-sánna

in ex-cél-sis. Be-ne-díc-tus, qui ve-nit in nó - mi-ne

Dó-mi-ni. Ho - sánna in ex-cél - sis.

Per ómni - a sǽ-cu-la sæ-cu-ló - rum. ℟. Amen.

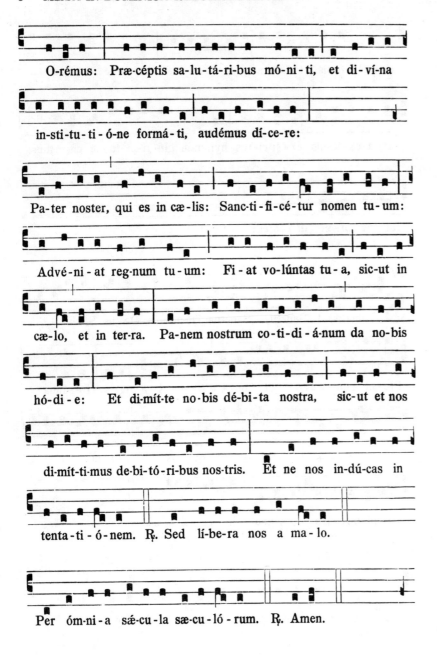

O-rémus: Præ-céptis sa-lu-tá-ri-bus mó-ni-ti, et di-ví-na

in-sti-tu-ti-ó-ne formá-ti, audémus dí-ce-re:

Pa-ter noster, qui es in cæ-lis: Sanc-ti-fi-cé-tur nomen tu-um:

Advé-ni-at reg-num tu-um: Fi-at vo-lúntas tu-a, sic-ut in

cæ-lo, et in ter-ra. Pa-nem nostrum co-ti-di-á-num da no-bis

hó-di-e: Et di-mít-te no-bis dé-bi-ta nostra, sic-ut et nos

di-mít-ti-mus de-bi-tó-ri-bus nos-tris. Et ne nos in-dú-cas in

tenta-ti-ó-nem. R̶. Sed lí-be-ra nos a ma-lo.

Per óm-ni-a sǽ-cu-la sæcu-ló-rum. R̶. Amen.

Pax ✠ Dó-mi-ni sit ✠ semper vo-bís-✠ cum. R̶. Et cum

spí-ri-tu tu-o.

IV

A g-nus De-i, * qui tol-lis peccá-ta mun-di:

mi-se-ré - - re no-bis. Agnus De-i, * qui tol-lis

peccá-ta mun-di: mi-se-ré - - re no-bis. Ag-nus

De-i, * qui tol-lis peccá-ta mun-di: do-na no - - bis

pa - cem.

Comm.
VI
P ascha nostrum * immo-lá-tus est Chris-tus,

al-le-lú-ja: í-ta - - que e-pu-lé-mur

in á-zy-mis sin-ce-ri-tá-tis et ve-ri-tá-tis,

al-le - lú-ja, al-le - -lú-ja, al-le-lú - ja.

Postcommunio

Spíritum nobis, Dómine, tuæ caritátis infúnde: † ut, quos sacra-
méntis paschálibus satiásti, * tua fácias pietáte concórdes. Per
Dóminum . . . in unitáte ejúsdem.

VIII

- te, Missa est, al·le-lú-ja, al-le - lú - ja.
℟. De-o grá-ti-as, al·le-lú-ja, al-le - lú - ja.

Kyrie (Clemens Rector)

I.

KYrie * e- lé- i-son. Ký- ri-

e e- lé- i-son. Ký- ri- e

e- lé- i-son. Chri- ste e- lé- i-son.

Chri-ste e- lé- i-son. Chri- ste

e- lé- i-son. Ký- ri- e

e- lé- i-son. Ký- ri- e

e- lé- i-son. Ký- ri- e * *

e- lé- i-son.

Dies irae
Sequence

Sequent. I.

DI- es i-rae, di- es il-la, Solvet saeclum in favíl-la : Teste Da-vid cum Si-býlla. Quantus tremor est fu-túrus, Quan-do ju-dex est ventúrus. Cuncta stricte discussúrus! Tuba mi-rum spar-gens sonum Per sepúlcra re-gi- ónum, Coget o-mnes ante thronum. Mors stupé-bit et na-tú-ra, Cum re-súrget cre-a-tú-ra, Ju-di-cán- ti responsú-ra. Li-ber scriptus pro- fe-ré-tur, In quo to-tum conti-né-tur, Unde

mundus ju-di-cé-tur. Ju-dex ergo cum se-dé-bit, Quidquid la-tet appa-ré-bit : Nil inúltum remané-bit. Quid sum mi-ser tunc dictú-rus? Quem patró-num roga-tú-rus? Cum vix ju-stus sit se-cúrus. Rex treméndae ma-jestá-tis, Qui salvándos salvas gra-tis, Salva me, fons pi- e-tá-tis. Re-cordá-re Je- su pi- e, Quod sum causa tu-ae vi-ae : Ne me per-das il-la di- e. Quaerens me, se- dí- sti lassus : Red-e-místi cru-cem passus : Tantus la- bor non sit cassus. Juste

10

ju-dex ul-ti- ó-nis, Do-num fac remissi- ó-nis,   Ante di- em

ra- ti- ó- nis.   Inge-mísco, tamquam re- us : Culpa ru-bet

vultus me- us : Suppli-cánti parce De- us.   Qui Ma- rí- am

absolvísti,   Et latró- nem exaudísti,   Mi-hi quoque spem

de- dísti.   Pre-ces me-ae non sunt dignae : Sed tu bo- nus

fac be-nígne,   Ne per-énni cremer igne.   Inter o-ves

lo- cum praesta,   Et ab haedis me sequéstra, Stá-tu- ens

in parte dextra.   Confu-tá- tis ma- le-dí-ctis, Flammis

ácri- bus addíctis : Vo-ca me cum be-ne-díctis.   O- ro

supplex et accli- nis, Cor contrí-tum qua-si ci-nis :   Ge- re

cu-ram me- i fi-nis.   Lacri-mó-sa di- es il-la, Qua re-súr-

get ex favíl- la,   Ju-di-cándus ho- mo re- us : Hu- ic

ergo par- ce De- us. Pi- e Je-su Dómi-ne, dona e- is

réqui- em. A- men.

a. Kyrie fons bonitatis

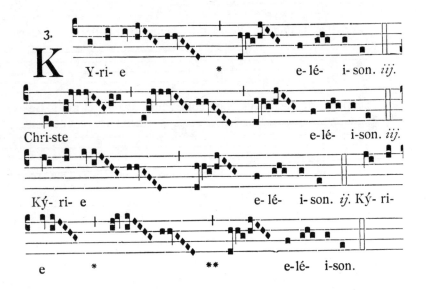

3. KYrie * elé- i-son. *iij.*

Chri-ste elé- i-son. *iij.*

Ký- ri- e elé- i-son. *ij.* Ký- ri-

e * ** elé- i-son.

b. Trope: Kyrie fons bonitatis

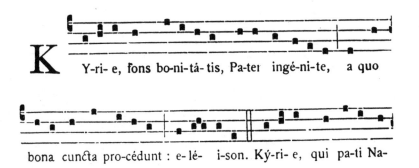

KYri- e, fons bo-ni-tá- tis, Pa-ter ingé-ni-te, a quo

bona cunɕta pro-cédunt : e-lé- i-son. Ký-ri- e, qui pa-ti Na-

tum mundi pro crími-ne, ipsum ut salvá-ret mi-sísti : e-lé-

i-son. Ký-ri- e, qui septi-fórmis dans dona Pnéuma-tis, a

quo cæ-lum, terra repléntur : e-lé- i-son. Christe, ú-ni-ce

De- i Patris Gé-ni-te, quem de Vírgi-ne nasci-tú-rum mundo

mi-rí- fi-ce sanɕti præ-di-xé-runt prophé-tæ : e-lé- i-son.

Christe hági- e, cæ-li compos régi- æ, me-los gló-ri- æ cu- i

semper adstans pro númi-ne Ange-ló-rum de-cántat a-pex :

e-lé- i-son. Christe cæ-li-tus adsis nostris pré-ci-bus, pro-

nis ménti-bus quem in terris devó-te có- limus, ad te pi- e

Je-su clamántes : e-lé- i-son. Ký- ri- e, Spí- ri-tus alme,

cohæ-rens Patri Na-tóque, u-ní- us u-sí- æ consisténdo, flans

ab utróque : e- lé- i-son. Ký- ri- e, qui bapti- zá- to in

Jordá-nis unda Chri-sto, effúlgens spé-ci- e co-lumbí-na ap-

pa-ru- ísti, e- lé- i-son. Ký- ri- e, ignis di-ví- ne, pécto-

ra nostra succénde, ut digne pá-ri-ter proclamá-re possímus

semper : e- lé- i-son.

O Roma nobilis
Goliard song

O Ro-ma no- bi- lis or- bis et do-mi- na. Cun-cta-rum ur-bi- um ex-

cel-len-tis-si- ma. Ro- se- o mar-ty- rum san-gui-ne ru-be- a. Al-

bis et li- li- is vir- gi-num can-di- da. Sa- lu-tem di- ci- mus ti-

bi per om-ni- a. Te be- ne- di- ci- mus sal- ve per se- cu- la.

Ce fut en mai
Lai

Moniot d'Arras, 13th century

Ce fut en mai, Au douz tens gai, Que la se-sons est be- le; Main me le-vai, Jo-

er m'a lai Lez u- ne fon- te- ne- le. En un ver-gier Clos d'es-glen-tier O-

i u-ne vi- e- le; La vi dan-cer Un che- va-lier Et u- ne de- moi-se- le.

Je la truis
Virelai

Je la truis trop as- pre- te, Voir, voir! A ceu k'elle est sim-

ple- te. Trop pour ou- tre cui- dies me tains Cant je cui-doie es-

tre cer- tains De ceu ke n'a ve- rai des mois, Oix! Oix! C'est

ceu ke plus me bles- ce. Or la truis trop as-

pre- te, Voir, voir! A ceu k'elle est sim- ple- te.

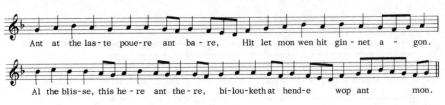

Ant at the las-te poue-re ant ba-re, Hit let mon wen hit gin-net a-gon.

Al the blis-se, this he-re ant the-re, bi-lou-keth at hend-e wop ant mon.

Ey ich sach in dem trone
Leich

Frauenlob, d. 1318.

Ey ich sach in dem tro-ne Ein jung-fraw die was swan-ger, Sie
Sie wol-te sin en-bun-den Suss gie die al-ler-bes-te, Zwolff

trug ein wun-der cro-ne In my-ner au-gen an-ger.
stei-ne zu der stun-den Koss in der kro-nen ves-te.

Nun mer-kent wie sie tru-ge die ge-fü-ge Der na-tur-en zu ge-
Sie tet auch waz sie sol-de ja die hol-de Sie trug den blu-men ein tol-de

nü-ge; Von dem sie was ge-bur-det Den sach sie vor ir sit-zen mit
fraw Meit ob ir mu-ter wür-det Des lam-mes und der tu-ben den

wit-zen In si-ben luch-ter-en; Und sach in doch ge-sun-dert In
tru-ben Ir lies-sent u-ver swe-ren Da-von mich nit en wun-dert Da

ey-nes lam-mes wy-se Uff sy-on dem ber-ge ge-hu-ren.
zuch dy-selb-(e) spy-se Kan zu der fruch-te ge-stu-ren.

Worldes blis

Worl-des blis ne last no thro-we, Hit wit ant wend a-wey a-non.

The leng-ur that hich hit i-kno-we, The lasse hic find-e pris ther-on.

For al hit is i-meynd wyd ka-re, Mid so-re-we ant wid u-vel fa-re.

Estampie

(b)

14

Sit gloria Domini
Strict organum

Sit glo - ri - a Do-mi - ni in sæ-cu-la: Læ-ta- bi-tur Do-mi-nus in o - pe-ri-bus su - is.

Rex cœli, Domine
Free organum

Rex cœ - li, Do - mi - ne   ma - ris un-di-so-ni,   Te hu - mi - les fa - mu - li,
Ti - ta - nis ni - ti - di   squa - li - di-que so - li,   Se ju - be - as fla - gi-tant

mo - du - lis ve - ne - ran-do pi - is,
va - ri - is li - be - ra - re ma-lis.

Benedicamus Domino
St. Martial organum

Be - - - ne - - - - - di -

ca - - - mus   etc.

Descendit de cœlis
Notre Dame organum

Des -

cen -

15

dit

de

cœ -

lis.

Sumer is icumen in
Rota

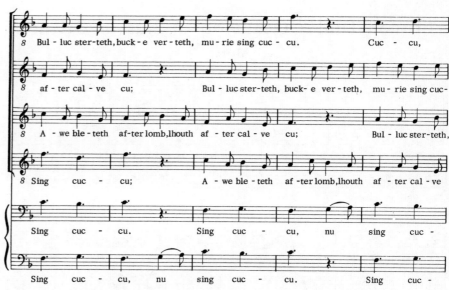

cuc - cu, Wel sing-es thu cuc - cu, ne swik thu na - ver nu.

cu. Cuc - cu, cuc - cu, Wel sing-es thu cu ___

buck - e ver - teth, mu - rie sing cuc - cu. Cuc - cu, cu ___

cu; Bul - luck ster - teth, buck - e ver - teth, mu - rie sing cuc - cu.

cu. Sing cuc - cu, nu sing cuc - cu.

cu, nu sing cuc - cu. Sing cuc - cu.

En non Diu! / Quant voi / Eius in Oriente
Motet

En non Diu! que que nus di - e, Quant voi l'her-be vert et le tans

Quant voi la rose es - pa - ni - e, L'her - be vert et le tans cler,

Eius in oriente —

cler, Et le ro - si - gnol chan - ter, A donc fine a - mors me

Et le ro - si - gnol chan - ter, A dont fine a - mors m'en - vi - e

pri - e Do - ce - ment d'u-ne jo - li - ve - té chan - ter: "Ma - ri -

De joi - e fere et me - ner, Car qui n'aime il ne vit mi - e;

ons, leis-se Ro - bim por moi a - mer!" Bien me doi a - dés pe -

Por ce se doit on pe - ner: D'a - voir a - mors a a - mi - e

ner Et cha - piau de fleus por - ter, Por si bele a - mi - e,

Et ser - vir et ho - ne - rer, Qui en joi - e veut du - rer.

Quant voi - la rose es - pa - ni - e, L'her - be vert et le tans cler.

En non Diu! que que nus die au cuer me tient li maus d'a - mer.

Toutes voies / Trop ai grieté / Je la truis

Motet

Tou-tes voi-es m'a a-mours as-sa-li, Et dist que j'a me-
Trop ai de grie-té pour che-li, Qui j'ai-
Je la truis trop as-pre -- te

rai; Si ne sai que j'en fe-rai, Car che-le
me sanz' re-pen-tir; aï-mi! Au cuer sench le

n'a cu-re de mi. Si ne l'ai pas de-sier-
tres douch mal jo-li; Pour quoi je di Nuit et

vi, Qu'en loi-au-té ser-vi l'ai, N'en-co
jour, et chant en-si: Da-me, vous m'a-vés sai-

re -- pas ne m'en fain-de -- rai. Puis k'a-mours le
si, Si vous proi mer-chi; J'ai a vous moult lonc tans sier-

veut en -- si, Mer-chi de la dou-chete a -- ten-drai.
vi: Loi-au -- ment sou-vie -- gne vous de mi!

Veri floris sub figura

Conductus

Ve -- ri flo -- ris sub fi -- gu -- ra,

Messe Notre Dame, Kyrie

Guillaume de Machaut, 1300-1377

8 quem pro - du - - - xit ra - dix pu - - ra, cle - ri

8 no - stri pi - a cu - - ra flo - rem fe - cit

8 my - sti - cum pre - ter u - sum la - i - cum, sen - sum

8 tra - hens tro - pi - cum flo - ris a na - tu - - ra.

Ky - ri - e

Ky - ri - e

Ky - ri - e

Ky - ri - e

Three times

Three times

Ma fin est mon commencement

Rondeau

Guillaume de Machaut, 1300-1377

23

82,8 Et   mon com - men - ce - ment   ma
6 Se   re - tro - grade et ein - si

fin.
fin.

Gram piant agli' ochi

Ballata

Francesco Landini, 1325-1397

1.5. Gram   pian - t'a -
4. Ma   ben ch'i'

1.5. Gram   pian - t'a -
4. Ma   ben ch' i'

- gli o-chi,   gre - ve do - gli al   co -
vi - va,   ma' non vo'   se - gui -

gli o-chi,   gre - ve do - gli al   co -
vi - va,   ma' non vo'   se - gui -

re   A - bon - da sen - pre l'a - ni - ma, si mo -
re   Se   non vo', chia - ra stel - la et   dol - ce a - mo -

re   A - bon - da sen - pre l'a - ni - ma, si mo -
re   Se   non vo', chia - ra stel - la et   dol - ce a - mo -

- re.
- re.

- re.
- re.

Tosto che l'alba

Caccia

Gherardello, 14th Century

2. Per que-st'a-mar' ed a-spra di-par-ti-
3. Chon-tra mia vol-glia du-ra questa vi-

O

Tos-to che l'al-ba

-ta;
-ta,

del bel gior-no ap-pa-re I-sve-glia li cac-cia-tor. "Su,

O

Chia-mo la mor-t'e non mi vol u-
Che mil-le mor-ti mi con-vien sen-

su, su, su, ch'egli e'l tem-po!" "Al-let-ta li

Tos-to che l'al-ba del bel gior-no ap-pa-re I-sveg-lia li

di-ti-
-re;
-re;

can, te, te, ta, te, Vi-o-la, te, Pri-me-ra, te!"

cac-cia-tor, "Su, su, su, su, ch'egli e'l tem-po!"

25

Ritornello

Iste Confessor

Fauxbourdon hymn

Guillaume Dufay, c. 1400-1474

1. I - ste con - fes - sor Do - mi - ni sa - cra - tus, fe - sta plebs cu - ius ce - le - brat per or - bem, ho - di - e lae - tus me - ru - it se - cre - ta scan - de - re cae - li.

2. Qui pi - us, pru - dens, hu - mi - lis, pu - di - cus, so - bri - us, ca - stus fu - it et qui - e - tus, vi - ta dum prae - sens ve - ge - ta - vit

* In fauxbourdon only the two outer parts were written, the performer of the middle voice improvising his part (in more or less parallel motion) at the interval of the fourth below the upper voice.

e - - ius cor -po - ris ar - - - tus.

e - - ius cor -po - ris ar - - - tus.

vit e - ius cor -po - ris ar - - - tus.

nos in pa - - ce mu - tans E-ve no - men.

Ave maris stella

Dunstable, c. 1370–1453

1. A - ve ma - ris stel - la, De - i ma - ter al - ma,

At - que sem - per Vir - go, Fe - lix ce - li por - ta.

2. Su - mens il - lud A - - - ve

Ga - bri - e - lis o - - re, fun - - - da

L' homme armé

L'hom - me, l'hom - me, l'hom -me ar - me, l'hom -me ar - me,

L'hom -me ar - me, doibt on dou - ter, doibt on dou - ter.

On a fait par - tout cri - er Que chas - cun se

viengue ar - mer D'un hau - bre - gon de fer.

Missa L' homme armé, Kyrie

Jean de Ockeghem, c. 1430–1495

Ky - ri - e

Ky - ri - e

Ky - ri - e

Ky - ri - e

Pange lingua

Hymn

Pan-ge lin-gua glo-ri-o - si Cor-po-ris my-ste-ri-um, San-gui-nis-que pre-ti-o - si,

Quem in mun-di pre-ti - um Fru-ctus ven-tris ge-ne - ro-si Rex ef - fu - dit gen - ti-um.

Missa Pange lingua, Gloria

Josquin des Prés, c. 1445-1521

Et in____ ter - ra pax _____ ho-mi-ni - bus bo-nae____

Et in____ ter - ra pax ho-mi-ni - bus bo -

Et in____ ter - ra pax _____ ho-mi - ni -

Et in____ ter - ra pax ho-mi-ni -

____ vo-lun____ - ta - tis.

____ nae vo-lun-ta - tis.

bus bo-nae____ vo - lun-ta - tis. Lau-da-mus te. Be-ne - di - ci - mus____ te.

bus bo - nae vo-lun-ta - tis _____ Lau-da-mus te. Be-ne-di -

Lau-da-mus te. Be-ne-di-ci-mus

Lau-da-mus te.

Ad-o-ra - mus____ te. Glo-ri-fi - ca-mus____ te, glo-ri-fi - ca - mus

ci-mus te. Ad-o-ra - mus____ te. Glo-ri-fi - ca-mus____

te. Ad-o-ra - mus te. Glo-ri-fi-ca-mus te.

Be-ne-di-ci-mus te. Ad - o-ra-mus te. Glo-ri-fi-ca-mus

te. Gra-ti-as a-gi - mus ti - bi

te. Gra-ti-as a-gi - mus ti-bi

Gra-ti-as a-gi - mus ti -

te. Gra-ti-as a-gi - mus ti -

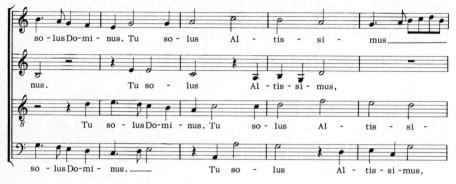

so - lus Do-mi - nus. Tu so - lus Al - tis - si - mus

nus. Tu so - lus Al - tis - si - mus,

Tu so - lus Do-mi - nus. Tu so - lus Al - tis - si -

so - lus Do-mi - nus. Tu so - lus Al - tis - si - mus,

tris, in glo-ri - a De - i Pa - tris. A - men.

- tris, in glo-ri - a De - i Pa - tris. A - men.

- tris, in glo-ri - a De - i Pa - tris. A - men.

tris, in glo-ri - a De - i Pa - tris. A - men.

Je - su Chri - ste. Cum San-cto Spi - ri - tu,

Je - su Chri - ste.

mus, Je - su Chri - ste. Cum San-cto Spi - ri -

Je - su Chri - ste. Cum

Zwischen Perg und tieffem Tal
Lied

Heinrich Isaac, c. 1450-1517

Zwi - schen perg und tie - ffem tal, zwi - schen perg und

Zwi - schen perg und tie - ffem

Zwi - schen perg

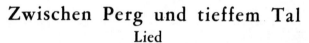

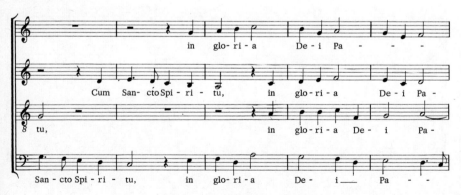

in glo-ri - a De - i Pa -

Cum San-cto Spi-ri - tu, in glo-ri - a De - i Pa -

tu, in glo-ri - a De - i Pa -

San-cto Spi - ri - tu, in glo-ri - a De - i Pa -

tie - ffem tal da ligt ein stra -

tal, zwi - schen perg und tie - ffem tal, da

Zwi - schen perg und

und tie - ffem tal

A ce ioly moys

Chanson

Clement Jannequin, c. 1475-c. 1560

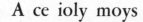
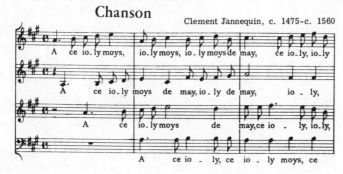

Quan die vous ayme ardentement

Jacob Arcadelt, c. 1514–c. 1570

Moro lasso

Don Carlo Gesualdo, c. 1560–1613

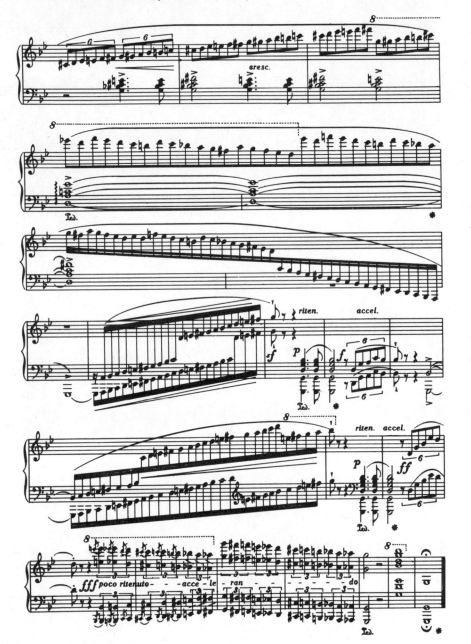

Excerpts from Carnaval

Papillons

Robert Schumann, 1810-1856 (Opus 9)

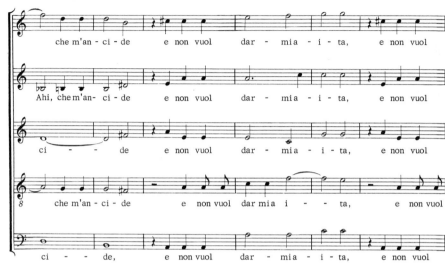

Please use this material instead of that which appears on pages 38 and 39 of the second printing of MUSIC SCORES OMNIBUS, Part 1, by Starr and Devine. (Pages 37 and 40 are correct.)

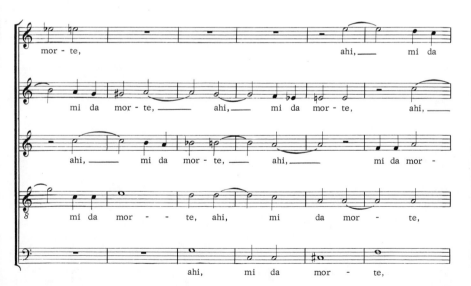

Look Down, O Lord

Full anthem

William Byrd, 1543-1623

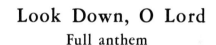

D.C. al Fine
a piacere

Lettres dansantes

Presto

Pavan and Galliard

Pavan

Thomas Morley, 1557–1602

Galliard

Rep.

The Silver Swan

Orlando Gibbons, 1583-1623

The sil - ver swan who, liv - ing, had no

The sil - ver swan who, liv - ing, had no note,_____

The sil - ver swan who, liv - ing, had no

The sil - ver_ swan who, liv - ing, had _____ no ___

The sil - ver swan who, liv - ing, had no

lock'd her si - lent throat:

si - lent throat: Lean - ing her

lock'd her si - lent throat: Lean -

lock'd_ her si - lent throat: a -

si - lent, si - lent throat: Lean - ing her

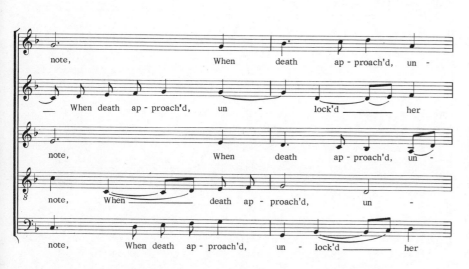

note, When death ap - proach'd, un -

_ When death ap - proach'd, un - lock'd _____ her

note, When death ap - proach'd, un -

note, When _____ death ap - proach'd, un -

note, When death ap - proach'd, un - lock'd _____ her

Lean - ing her breast a -

breast a - gainst the reed - y

- ing her breast a - gainst _____ the

gainst the reed - y shore, _____

breast a - gainst the reed - y

Penitential Psalm No. 6
(De profundis)

Orlando di Lasso (1532-1594)

5.

Su - sti - nu - it a - ni -

Su - sti - nu - it a - ni - ma me -

Su - sti - nu - it, su - sti - nu - it a -

Su - sti - nu - it, su - sti - nu -

Su - sti - nu - it a - ni - ma me -

6.

A cu - sto - di - a ma - tu - ti - na us -

A cu - sto - di - a ma - tu - ti - na us que ad

A cu - sto - di - a ma - tu -

A cu - sto - di - a ma - tu - ti - na us que ad

A cu - sto - di - a ma - tu - ti - na

ma me - a in ver - bo e - jus: spe - ra -

- a in ver - bo e - jus: spe - ra - vit a -

- ni - ma me - a in ver - bo e - jus: spe - ra - vit

it a - ni - ma me - a in ver - bo e - jus: spe - ra - vit a -

a in ver - bo e - jus: spe - ra - vit a -

- que ad no - ctem, us - que ad no - ctem: spe - ra -

no - ctem, us - que ad no - ctem, us - que ad no - ctem: spe - ret

ti - na us - que ad no - ctem: spe -

no - ctem, us - que ad no - ctem, us - que ad no - ctem: spe - ret

us - que ad no - ctem, us - que ad no - ctem: spe - ret Is - ra -

vit a - ni - ma me - a in Do - mi - no, in Do - mi - no.

- ni - ma me - a, a - ni - ma me - a in Do - mi - no.

a - ni - ma me - a, a - ni - ma me - a in Do - mi - no.

- ni - ma me - a, spe - ra - vit a - ni - ma me - a in Do - mi - no.

ni - ma me - a in Do - mi - no.

- ret Is - ra - el, spe - ret Is - ra - el in Do - mi - no.

Is - ra - el, spe - ret Is - ra - el in Do - mi - no, in Do - mi - no.

ret Is - ra - el in Do - mi - no.

Is - ra - el in Do - mi - no, spe - ret Is - ra - el in Do - mi - no.

el in Do - mi - no, spe - ret Is - ra - el in Do - mi - no.

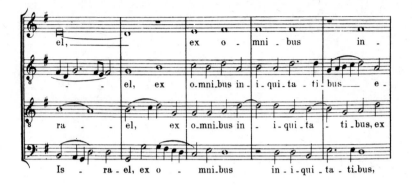

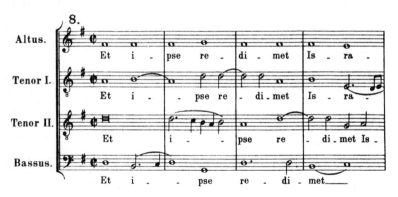

Lauda Sion

Motet a 4

Giovanni Pierluigi da Palestrina, c. 1524–1594

Missa Lauda Sion

Giovanni Pierluigi da Palestrina, c. 1524–1594

Gloria.

Credo.

Benedictus.

Agnus Dei I.

Agnus Dei II.

5 vocum.

Sonata Pian e Forte

Giovanni Gabrieli, 1557–1612

63

Amarilli mia bella
Continuo madrigal

Giulio Caccini, c. 1548–1618

A - ma - ril - li mia bel - la, Nó cre-di ò del mio cor dol-

ce de - si - o: D'es - ser tu l'a-mor mi - o. Cre - di - lo

pur, è se ti - mort'as-sa - le, Pren - dí que-sto mio stra - le, A pri-m'il

pet - to,è ve-drai scrit-to il co - re: A-ma - ril - li, A-ma-

Cruda Amarilli

Madrigal

Claudio Monteverdi, 1567-1643

ril - li, A-ma-ril-lièil mioa mo - re! Cre - di - lo

11 #10 14 # 7 #6

pur e se ti - mor t'as-sa - le, Pren-di que-sto mio stra-le, A - pri-m'il

7 6 6 5

Cru - da Ama-ril-li Cru - da Ama-

Cru - da Ama-ril-li Cru - da Ama-

Cru - da Ama-ril - li Cru - da Ama-

Cru - da Ama-ril - li Cru - da Ama-

Cru - da Ama-ril - li Cru - da Ama-

pet - toè ve-drai scrit-toil co - re: A-ma-ril - li, A-ma-

11 #10 14

ril - li, A-ma-ril-lièil mioa-mo - re, A-ma-

11 #10 14

-ril - li Che col no-me an-co-ra D'a - mar

-ril - li Che col no-me an-co-ra D'a - mar ahi

-ril - li Che col no-me an-co-ra D'a - mar ahi

-ril - li Che col no-me an-co-ra D'a - mar ahi

ril - lièil mioa-mo - re!

11 #10 14

69

70 CRUDA AMARILLI, Monteverdi

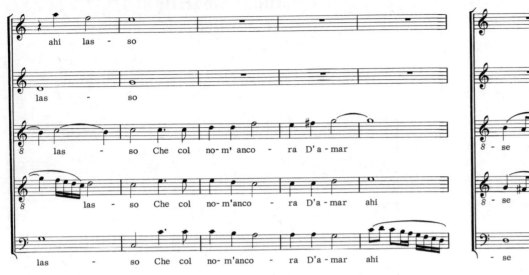

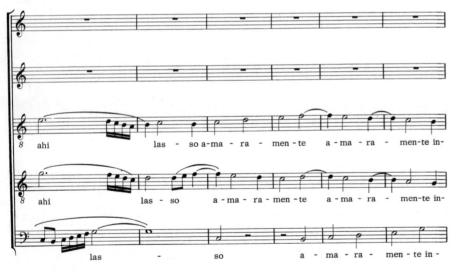

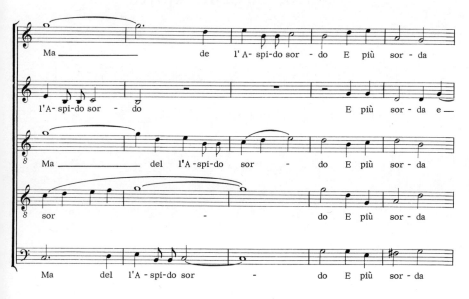

Orfeo, Possente spirto

Claudio Monteverdi, 1567-1643

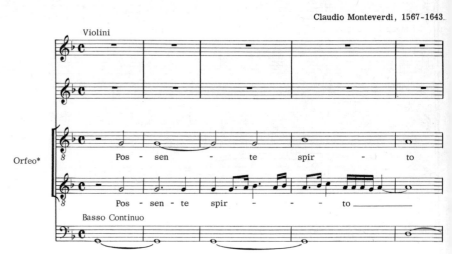

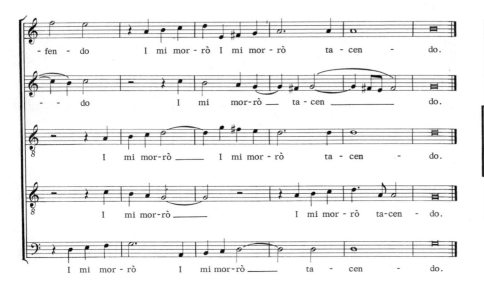

* The lower of the two voice lines illustrates, with Monteverdi's own musical text, contemporary performance practice with regard to embellishments.

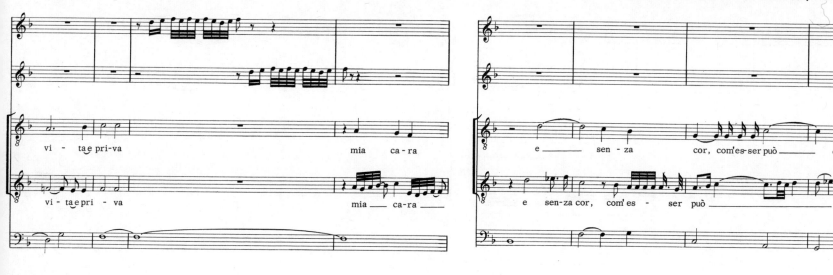

vi - ta e pri-va   mia ca - ra

vi - ta e pri - va   mia ca - ra

e ____ sen - za   cor, com'es-ser può ____   ch'io vi - va.

e sen-za cor, com'es - ser può _____ ch'io vi - va.

spo - sa,   il cor ____ non e più me - co

spo - sa,   il cor   non e ____ più me - co

Ritornello

Il pomo d'oro, Act I, Scene I

Marc' Antonio Cesti, 1623-1669

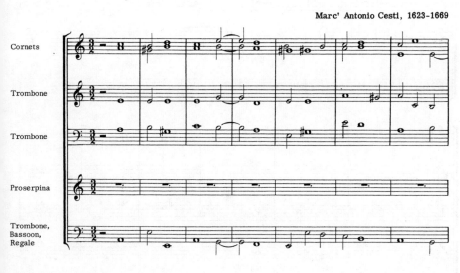

Jephte, Recitative and final chorus

Giacomo Carissimi, 1605-1674

Historicus. Cum vi-disset Jephte, qui votum Do-mi-no vo-ve-rat, fi-li-am su-am ve-ni-en-tem in oc-cur-sum, præ do-lo-re et la-chri-mis sci-dit ve-sti-men-ta su-a et a-it:

Jephte. Heu, heu mi-hi! fi-li-a me-a, heu de-ce-pi-sti me, fi-li-a u-ni-ge-ni-ta, de-ce-pi-sti me, et tu pa-ri-ter, heu fi-li-a me-a, de-cep-ta es, de-cep-ta es.

Filia. Cur e-go te pa-ter de-ce-pi et cur er-go fi-li-a tu-a u-ni-ge-ni-ta de-cep-ta sum?

Jephte. A-pe-ru-i os me-um ad Do-mi-num, ut quicumque primus de do-mo me-a oc-cur-re-rit mi-hi, of-fe-ram il-lum Domino in ho-lo-cau-stum. Heu mihi! fi-li-a me-a, heu de-ce-pi-sti me, fi-li-a u-ni-ge-ni-ta, de-ce-pi-sti me, et tu pa-ri-ter, heu fi-li-a me-a, de-cep-ta es, de-cep-ta es.

85

Attilio Regolo, Sinfonia

2.B.

Alessandro Scarlatti, 1660-1725

Sonata, A major, Longo 491

Domenico Scarlatti, 1685-1757

Symphoniae Sacrae, No. X

Chromatic fantasia

Jan Pieterszoon Sweelinck, 1562–1621

Fiori musicali, Ricercar dopo il credo

Girolamo Frescobaldi, 1583-1643

Excerpt from Dido and Aeneas

N⁰ 33   RECITATIVE

Henry Purcell, c. 1659-1695

DIDO

Thy hand, my An..na; dark.....ness shades me: On thy bo..som let me

rest: More I would, but Death in..vades me. Death is now a welcome guest!

N⁰ 34.   SONG.

DIDO

When I am laid, am laid..... in

pp (Ground Bass)

LARGHETTO

earth, may my wrongs cre...ate No trouble, no trouble in thy breast; Re..

...member me, re..member me, but ah!... for.....get.... my

fate. Re..member me, but ah!... for.....get my fate.

EXCERPT FROM DIDO AND AENEAS, Purcell

End of the Opera.

In dulci jubilo

Chorale prelude

Dietrich Buxtehude, 1637–1707.

Concerto, C Minor

Arcangelo Corelli, 1653-1713 (Opus 6, No. 3)

105

Les Tourbillons

Jean-Philippe Rameau, 1683-1764

L'Auguste from Premier Ordre

François Couperin, 1668-1733

Allemande.

Excerpt from St. Matthew Passion

Johann Sebastian Bach, 1685-1750

RECITATIVO. CORO I.

CORO I. II.

Brandenburg Concerto No. II, F Major

Johann Sebastian Bach. 1685-1750

Tromba.

Flauto.

Oboe.

Violino.

Violino I.
di ripieno.

Violino II.
di ripieno.

Viola
di ripieno.

Violone
di ripieno.

Violoncello
e Cembalo
all'unisono.

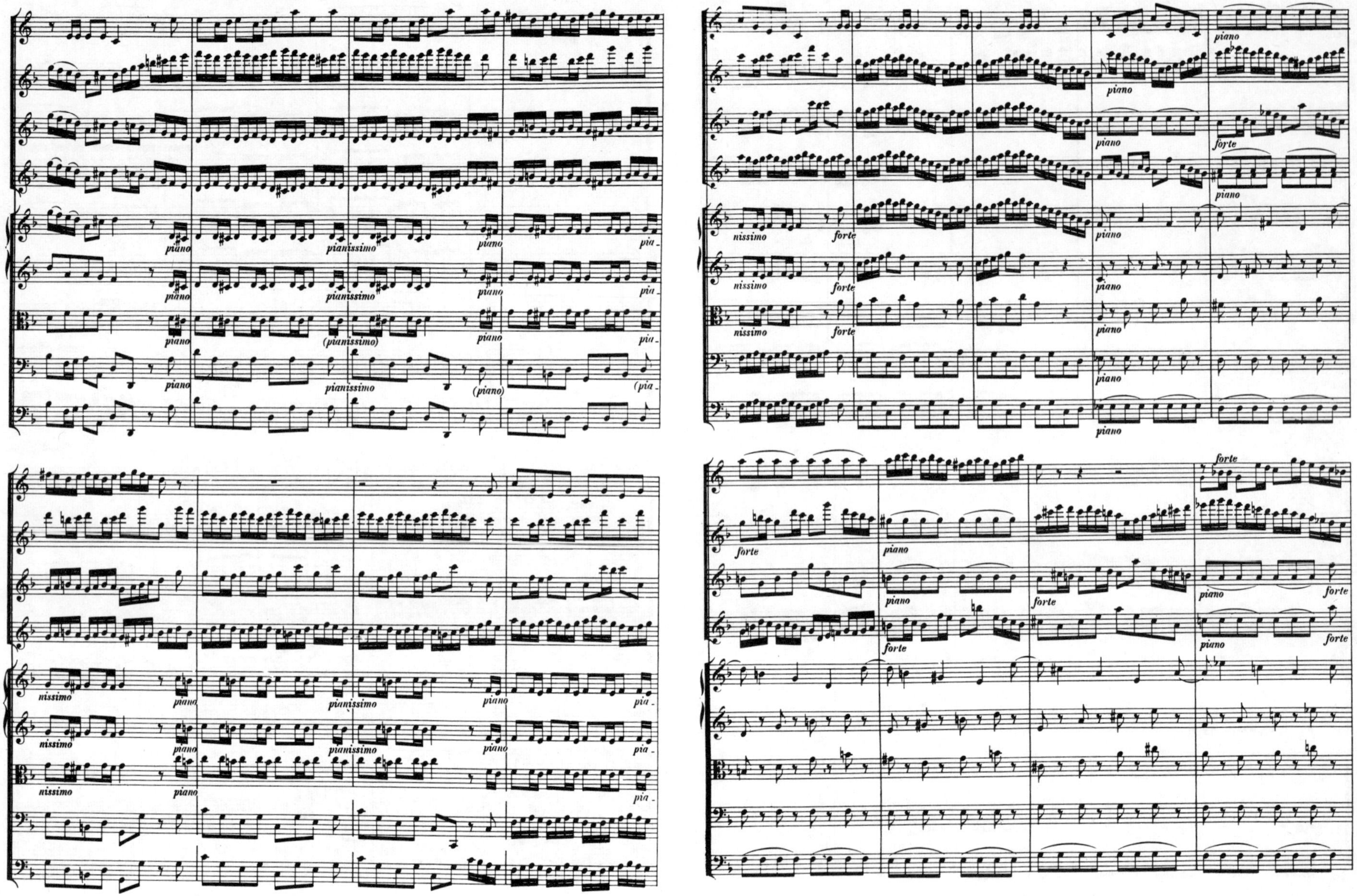
piano
pianissimo
(pianissimo)
(piano)
pia_
nissimo
forte

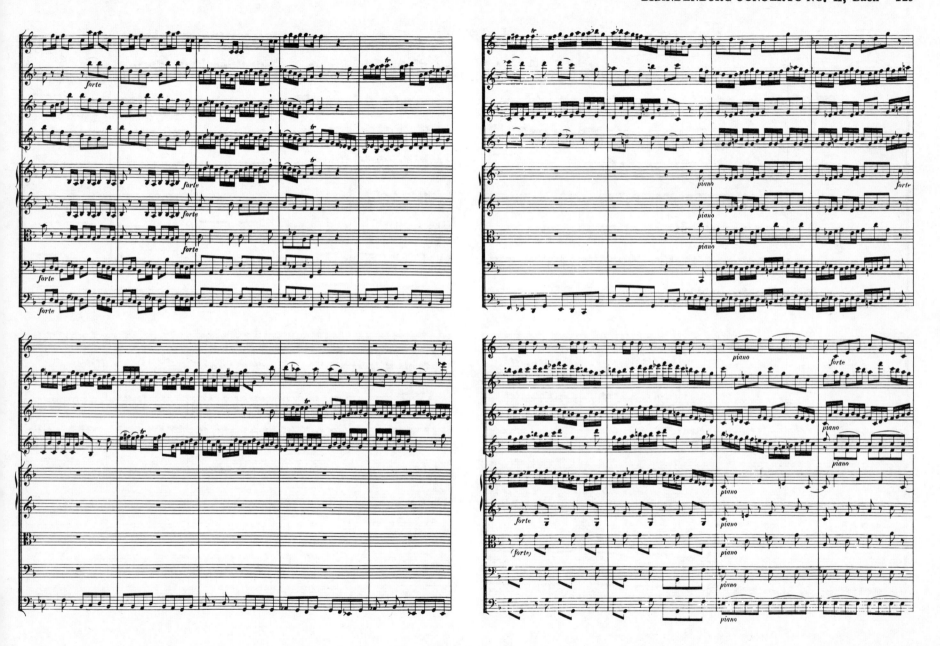

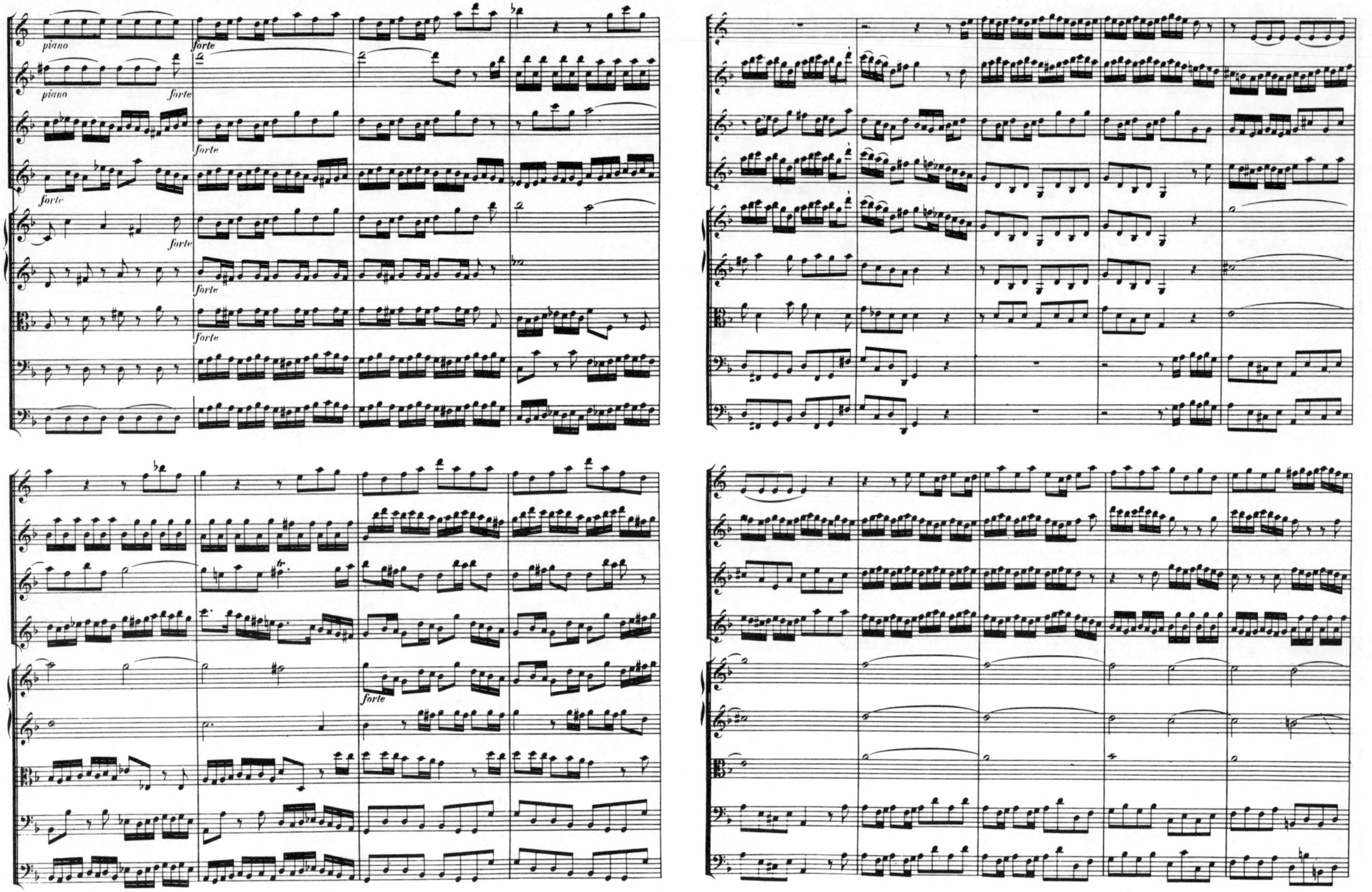
piano
piano
forte
forte
forte
forte
forte
forte
tr.
forte

Allegro assai.

Tromba.
Flauto.
Oboe.
Violino.
Violino I.
di ripieno.
Violino II.
di ripieno.
Viola
di ripieno.
Violone
di ripieno.
Violoncello
e Cembalo.

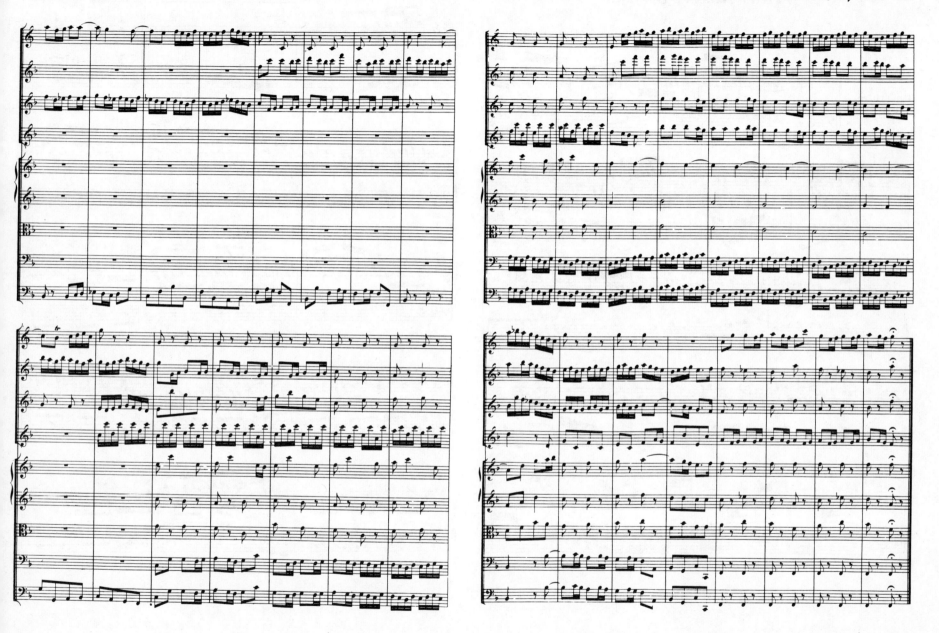

Partita No. IV, D Major

Johann Sebastian Bach. 1685-1750

Allemande.

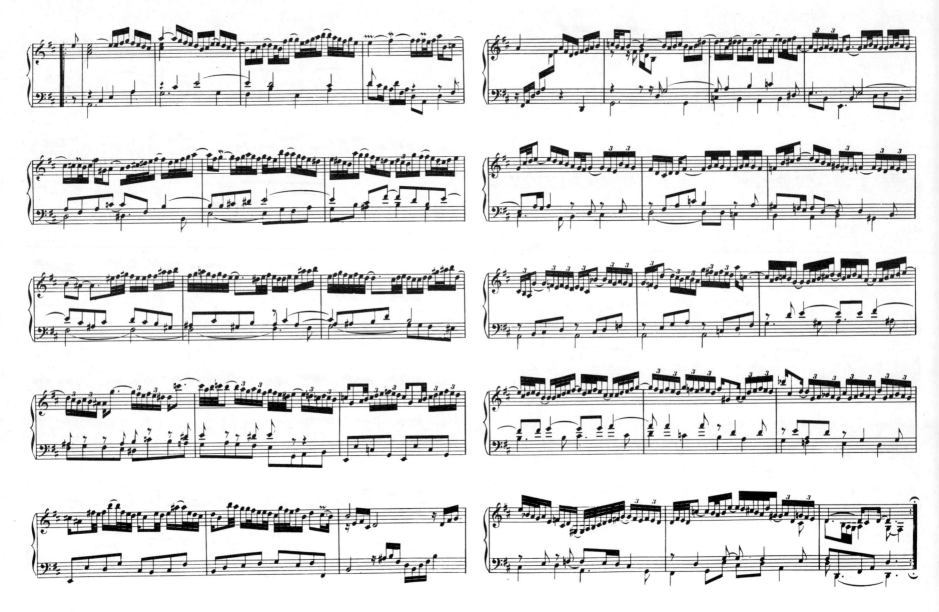

Aria.

Sarabande.

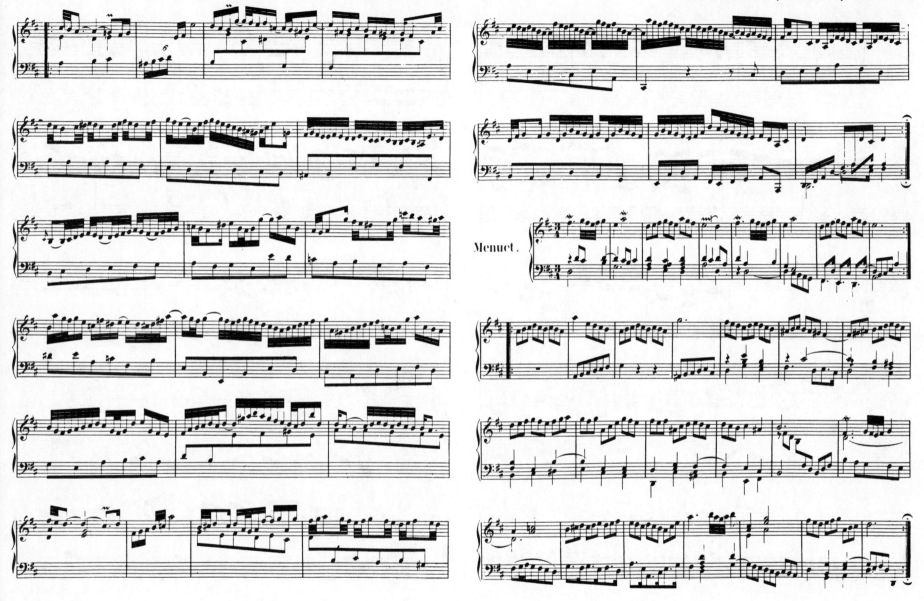

Menuet.

Gique.

In Dulci Jubilo

Johann Sebastian Bach. 1685-1750

Durch Adam's Fall ist ganz verderbt

Ein feste Burg ist unser Gott

Johann Sebastian Bach, 1685-1750

Johann Sebastian Bach, 1685-1750

149

Wenn wir in höchsten Nöthen sein

Vor deinen Thron tret ich

Johann Sebastian Bach. 1685-1750

Johann Sebastian Bach. 1685-1750

Choral

Choral

Cantata No. 80, Ein feste Burg ist unser Gott

Johann Sebastian Bach, 1685-1750

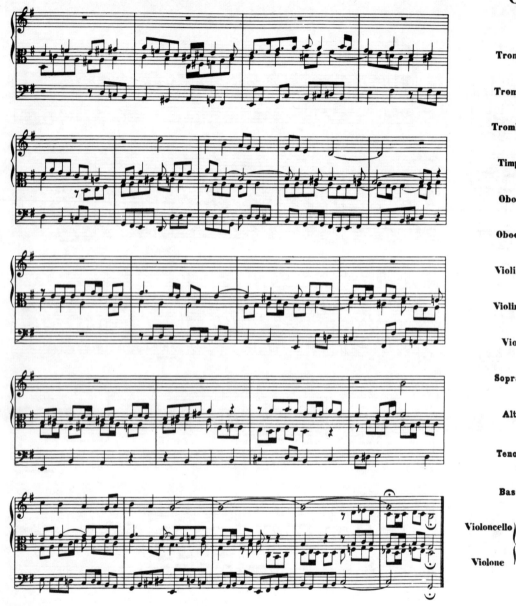

ARIA.

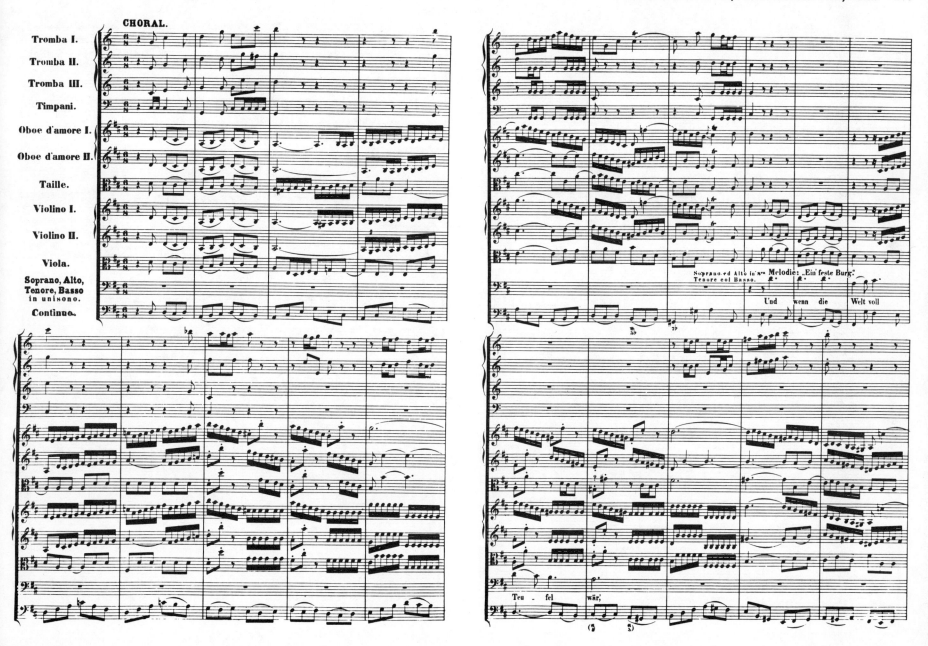

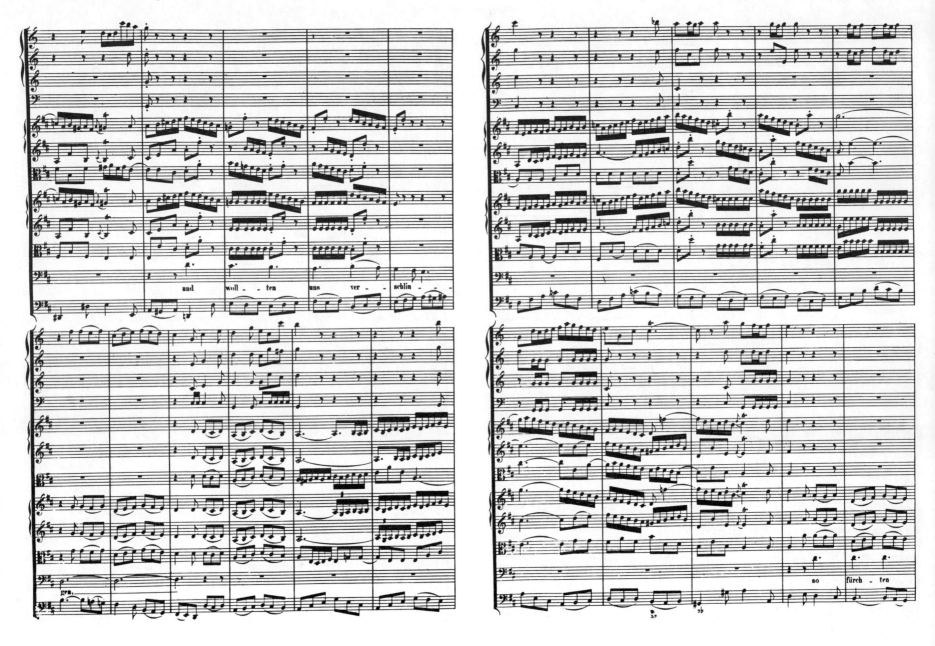

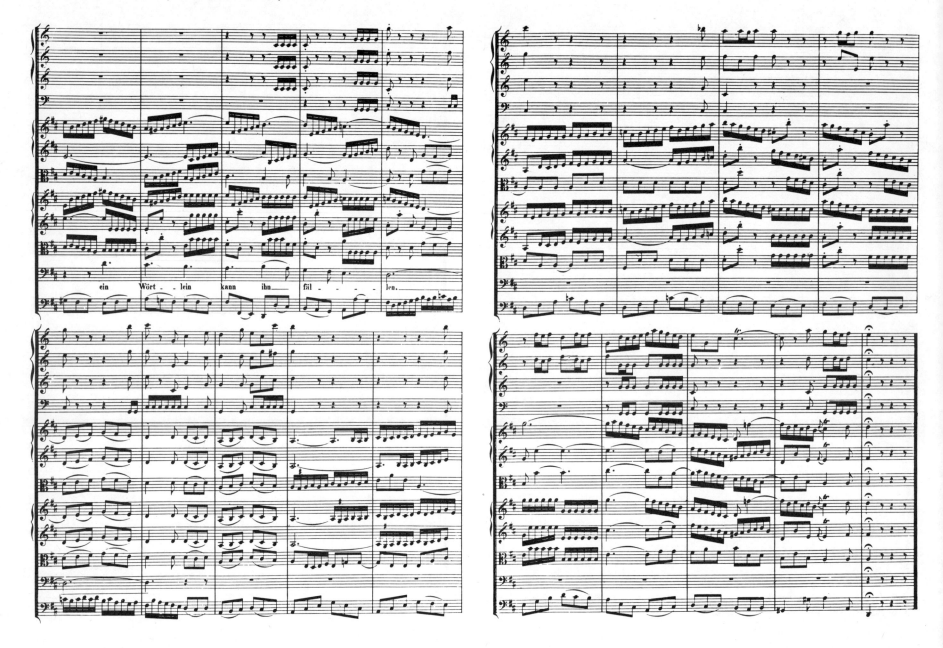

ein   Wört _ lein   kann   ihn ___ fäl _ _ _ len.

Prelude and Fugue, C Major

Johann Sebastian Bach, 1685-1750

Dal Segno.

CHORAL. Melodie: „Ein' feste Burg."

FUGA I.

Prelude and Fugue, C Minor

Johann Sebastian Bach, 1685-1750

184

FUGA II

Prelude and Fugue, E Flat Minor

Johann Sebastian Bach, 1685-1750

FUGA VIII

Sonata for Two Oboes and Continuo, B Flat Major

George Frederick Handel. 1685-1759

Israel in Egypt, Chorus: Who Is Like Unto Thee, O God

George Frederick Handel. 1685-1759

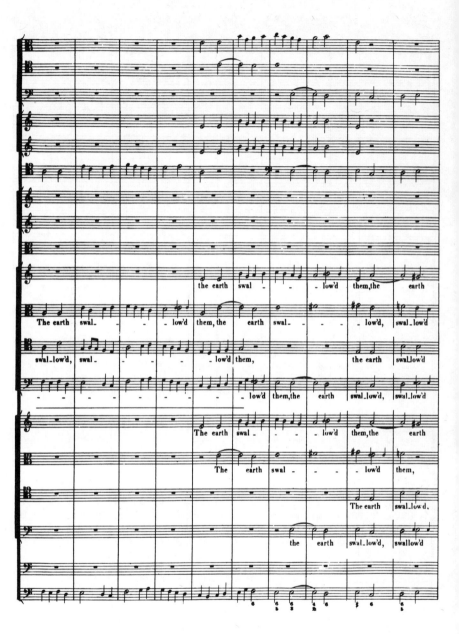

Rinaldo, Aria: Ogni indugio d'un amante

George Frederick Handel. 1685-1759

String Quartet, F Major

Franz Joseph Haydn. 1732-1809 (Opus 3. No. 5)

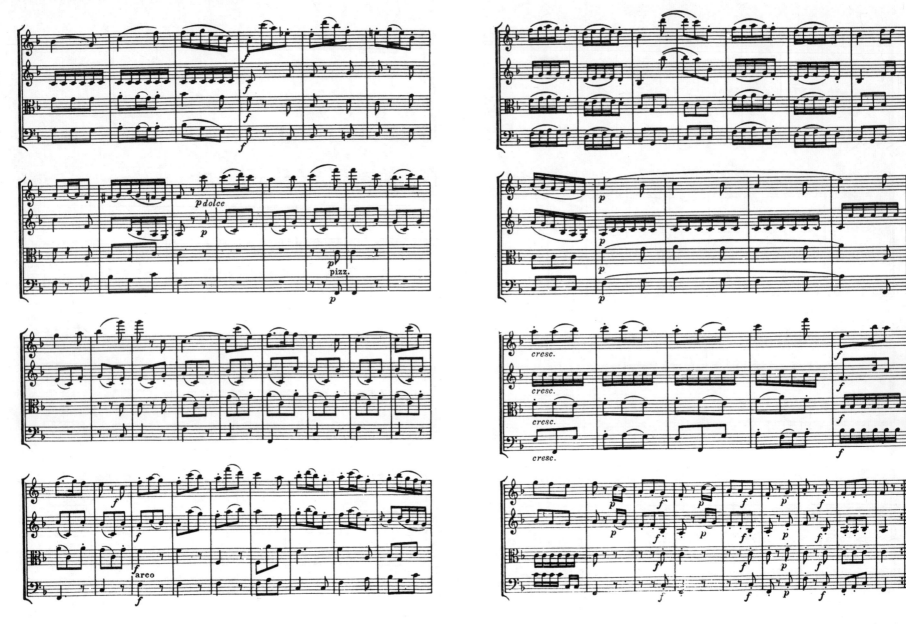

M. D. C.

Scherzando

Symphony No. 104, D Major (London Symphony)

Franz Joseph Haydn, 1732-1809

* The piano part in this score is not a part of Haydn's instrumentation. It is a two-stave reduction of the score included because 1) it will prove a help to students analyzing this work and 2) it provides a model for the making of such reductions of other orchestral compositions.

String Quartet, D Minor (K. 421)

Wolfgang Amadeus Mozart. 1756-1791

Piano Concerto, B Flat Major (K. 595), First Movement

Wolfgang Amadeus Mozart, 1756-1791

Piano Sonata, D Major (K. 576)

Wolfgang Amadeus Mozart, 1756-1791

Excerpt from The Marriage of Figaro

Wolfgang Amadeus Mozart , 1756-1791

Ouverture.

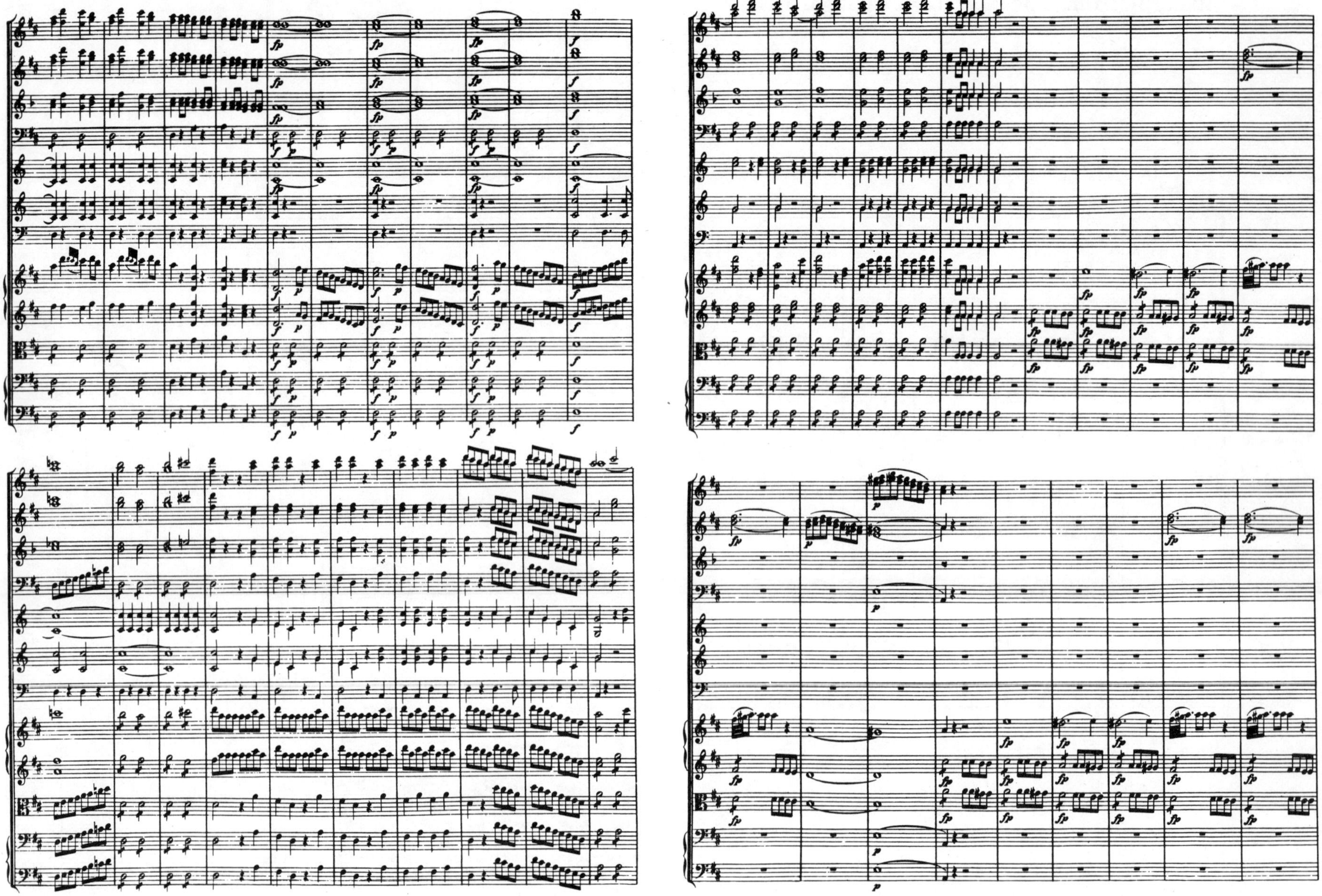

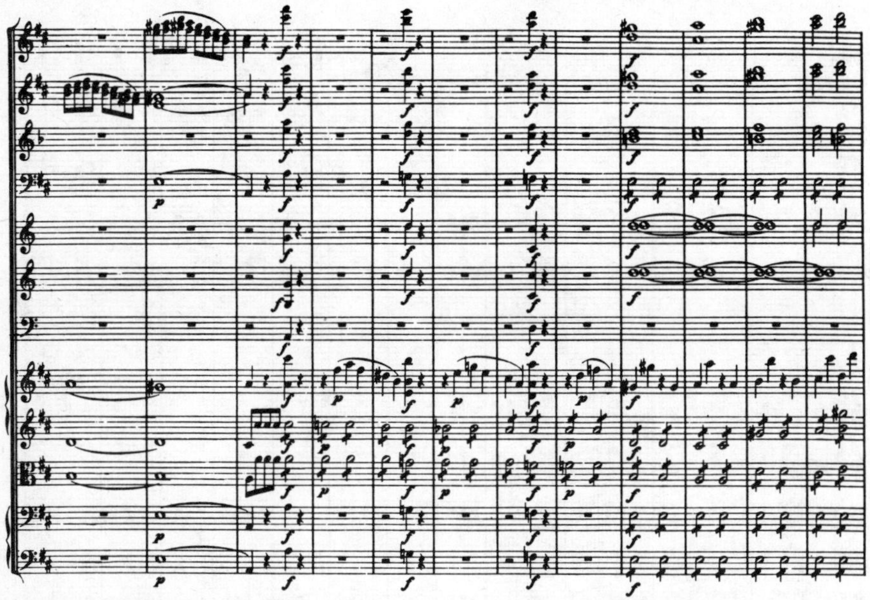

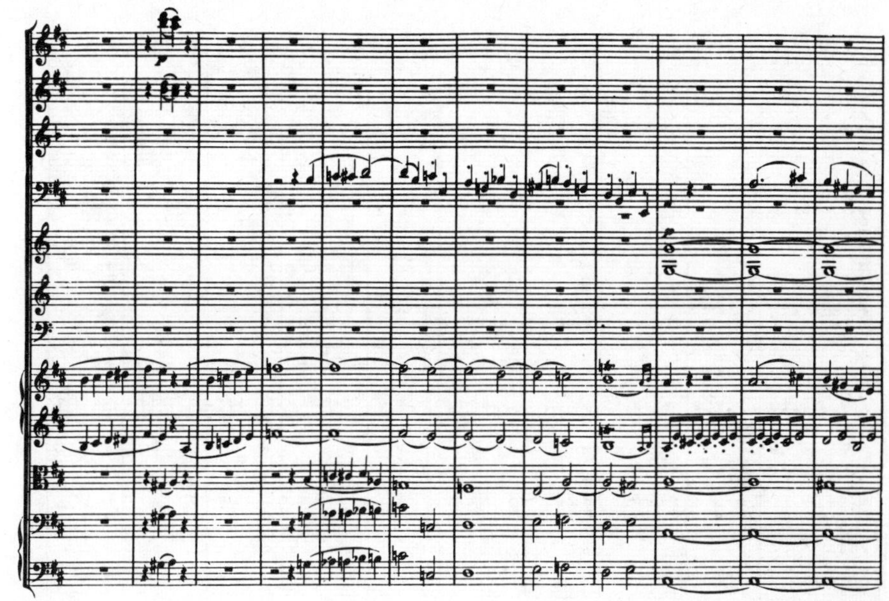

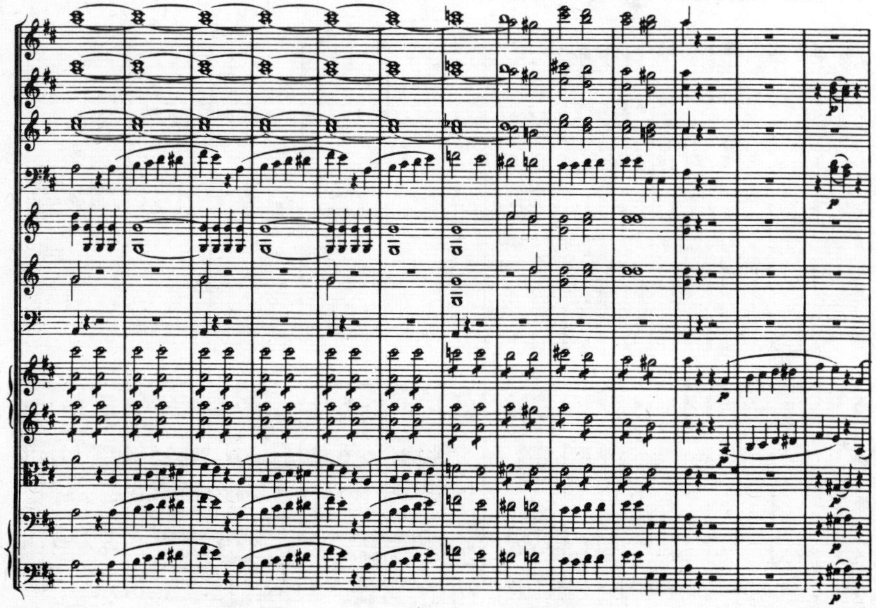

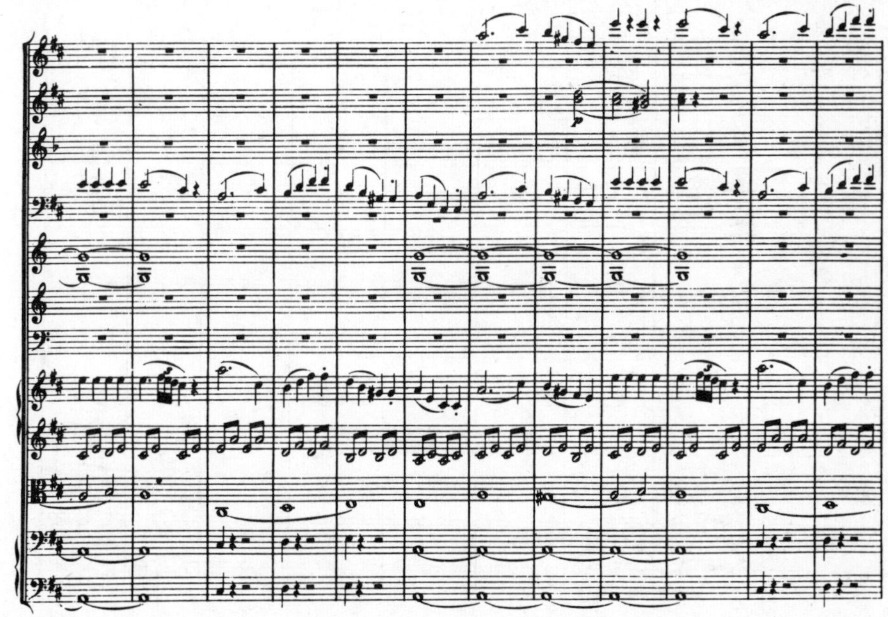

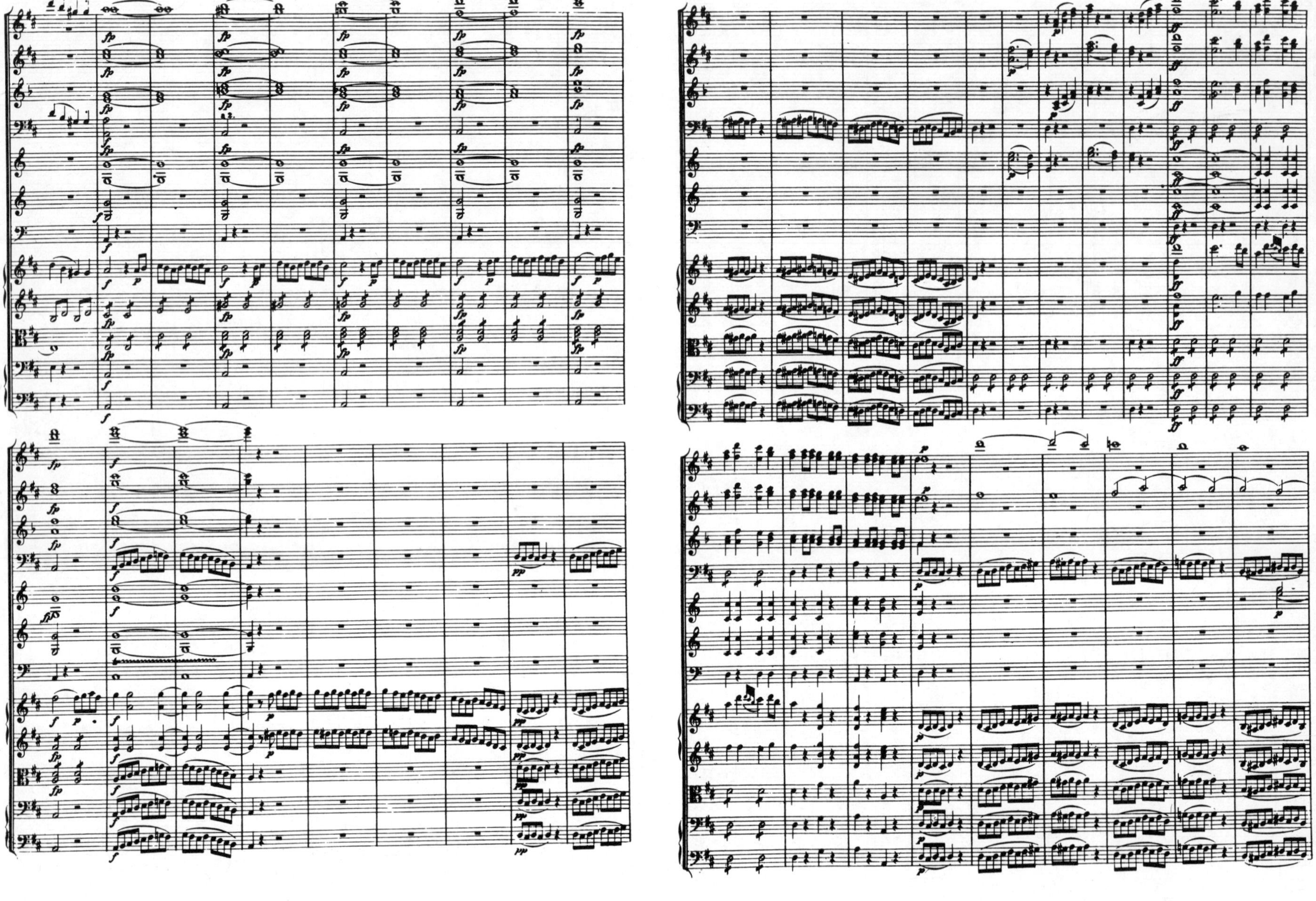

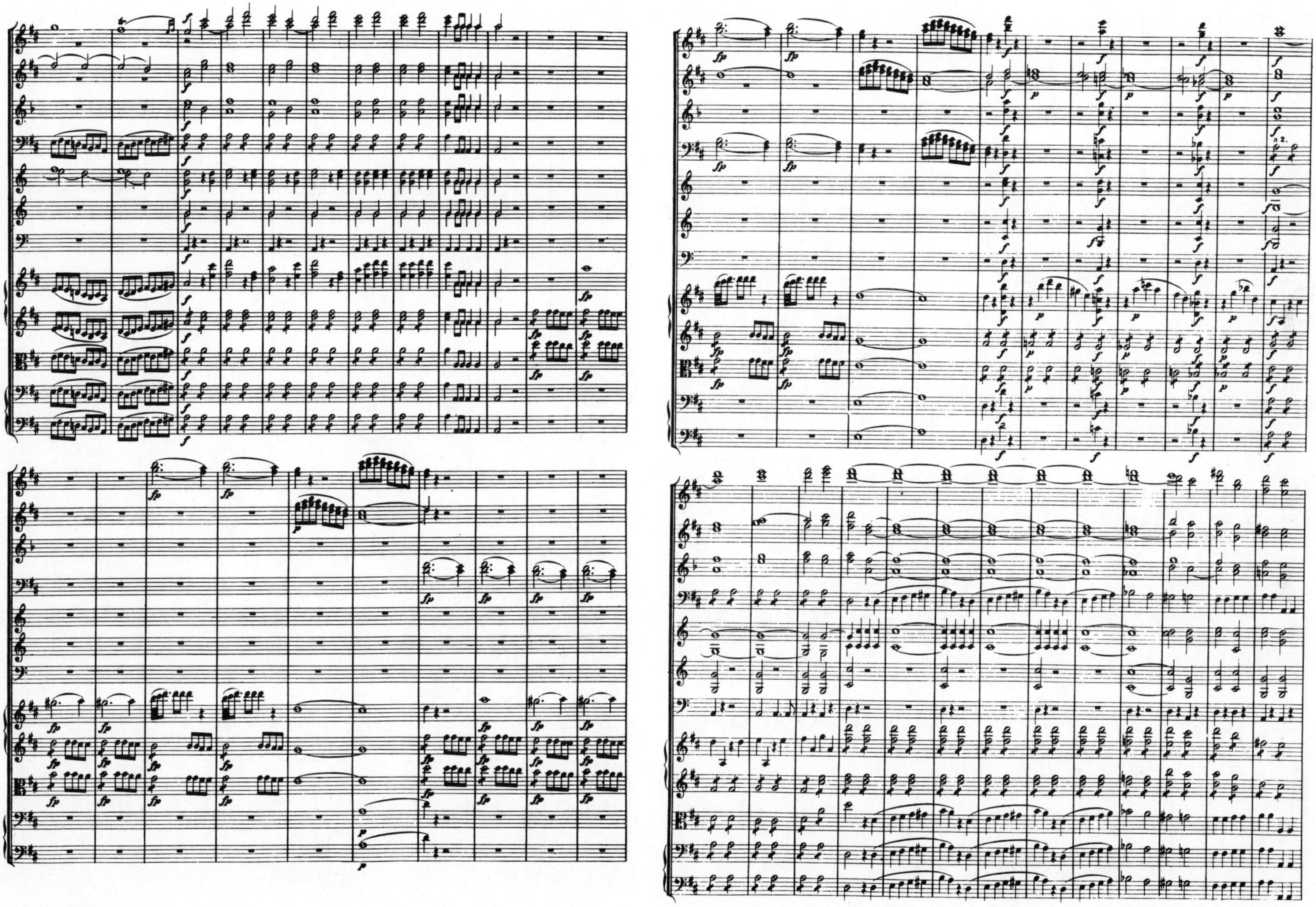

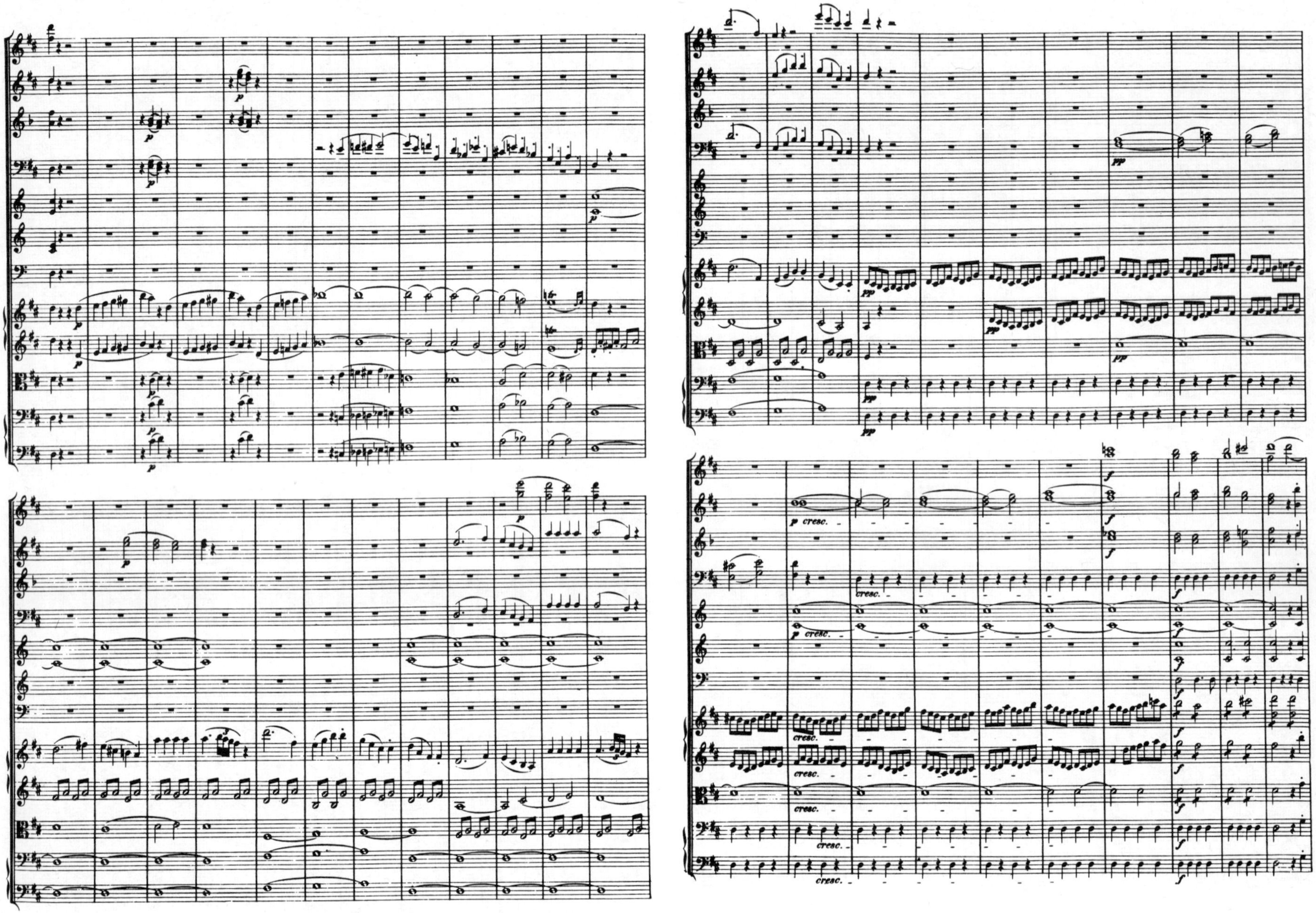
p cresc.
cresc.

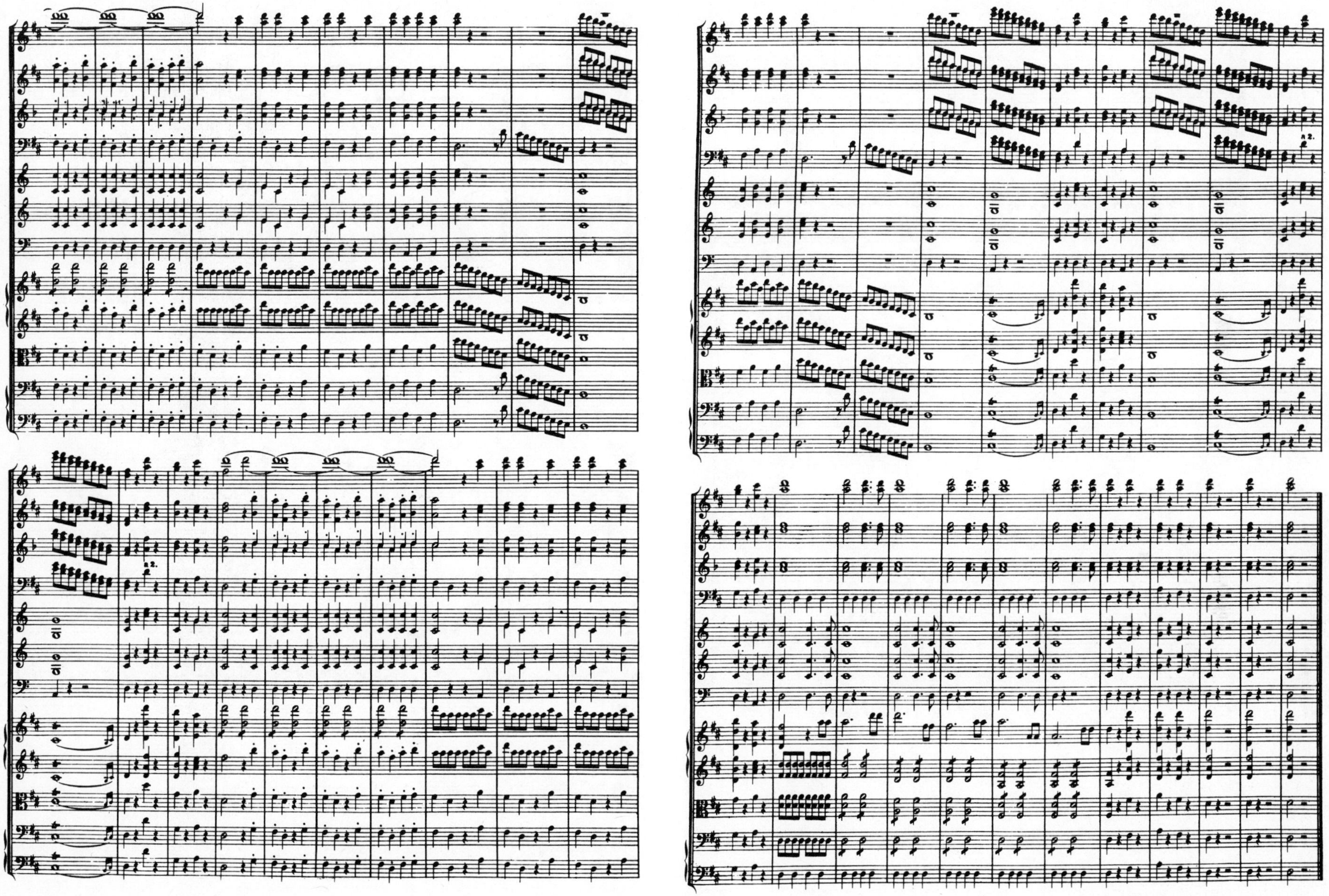

Nº 1. Duettino.
Allegro.

Flauti.

Oboi.

Fagotti.

Corni in G.

Violino I.

Violino II.

Viola.

SUSANNA.
SUSANNA.

FIGARO.
FIGARO.

Violoncello e
Basso.

Recitativo.

Nº 2. Duettino.
Allegro.

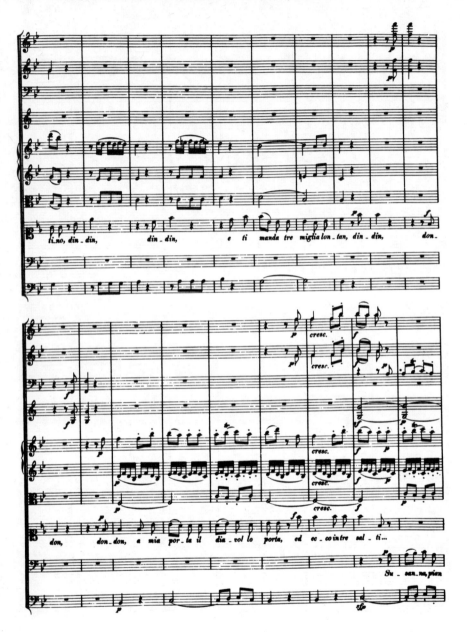

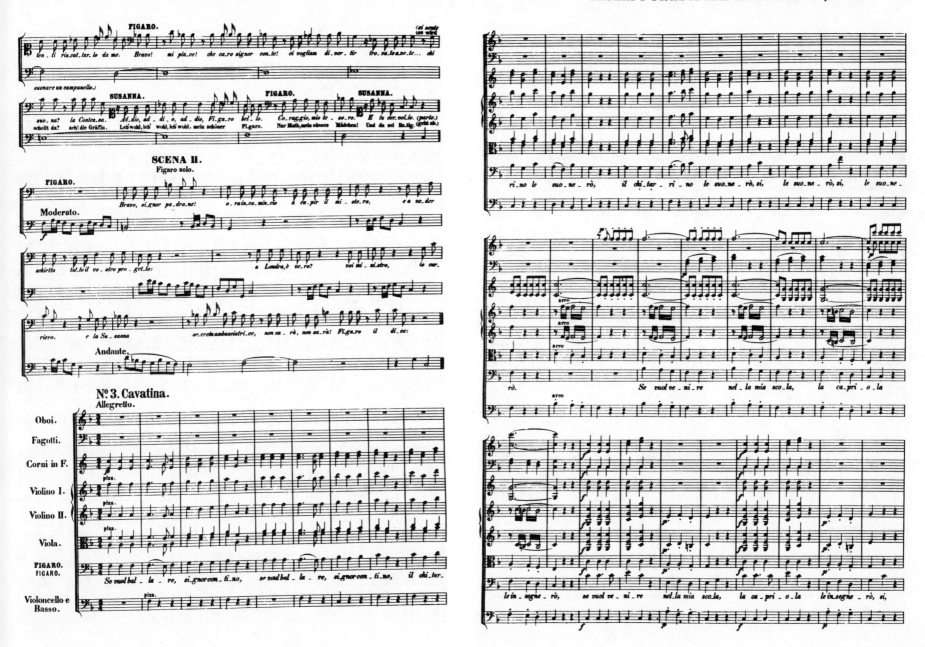

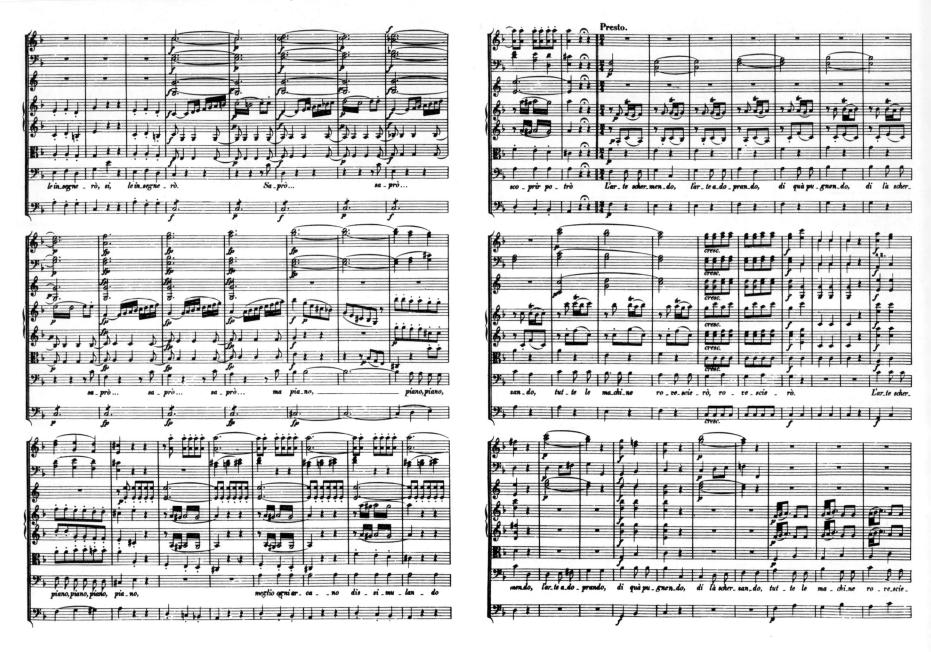

Sketches for First Movement, Quartet in F Major

Ludwig van Beethoven, 1770–1827 (Opus 18, No. 1)

String Quartet, F Major, First Movement

Ludwig van Beethoven, 1770–1827 (Opus 18, No. 1)

String Quartet, B Flat Major

Ludwig van Beethoven, 1770-1827 (Opus 130)

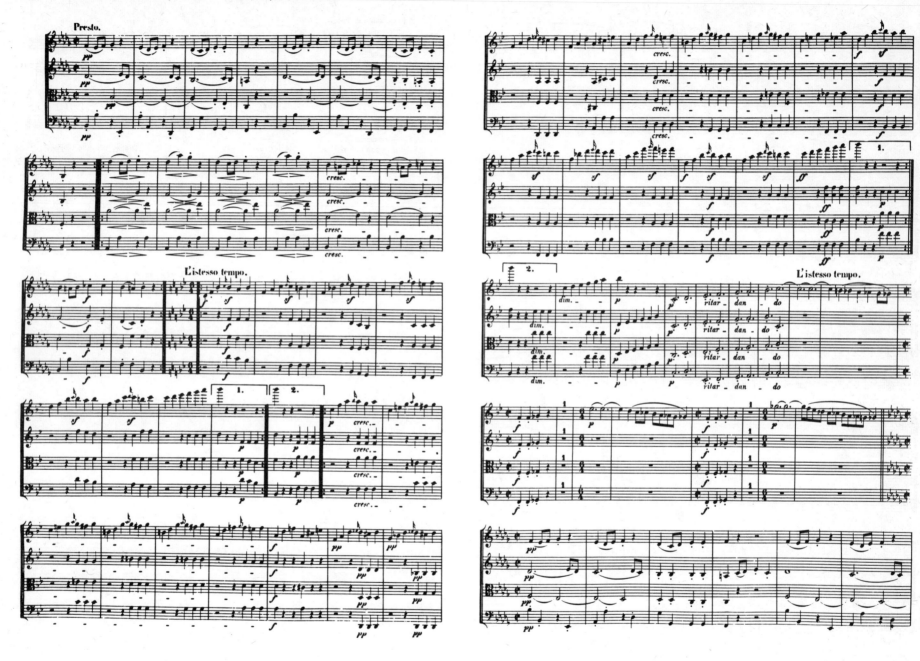

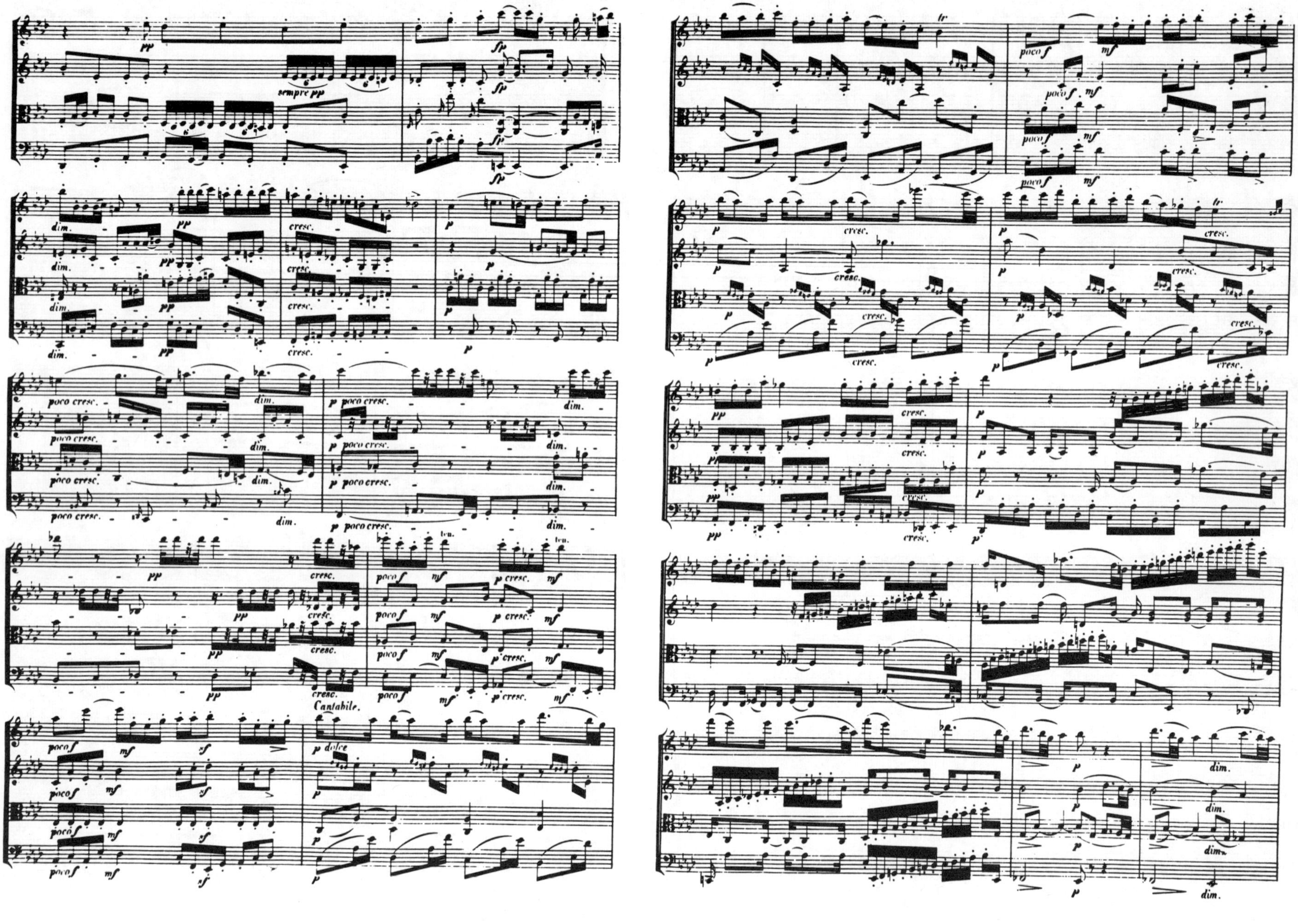
pp
sempre pp
sf
dim.
cresc.
p
poco cresc.
ten.
poco f
mf
Cantabile
p dolce
tr

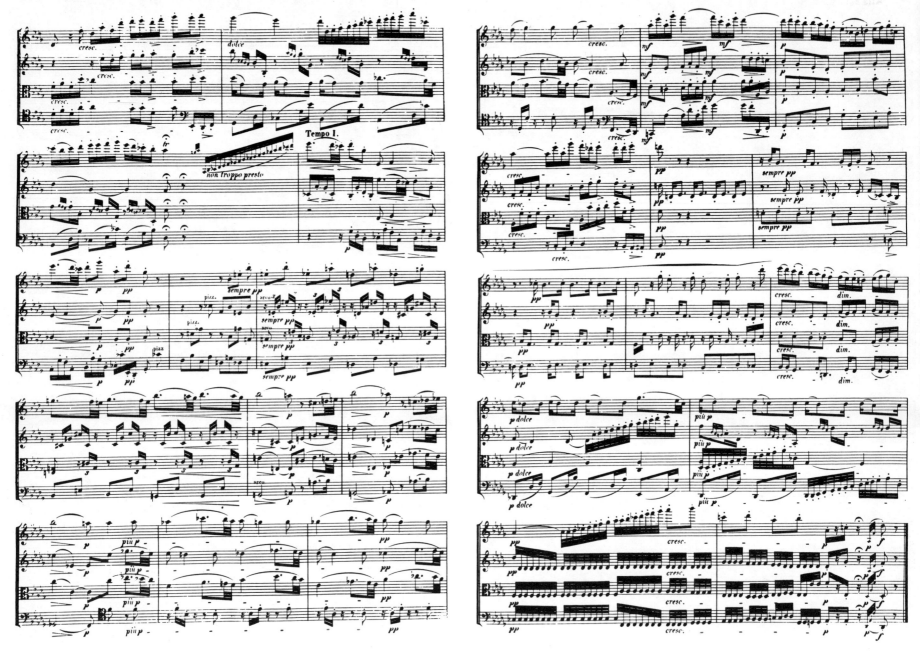

Alla danza tedesca.

Allegro assai.

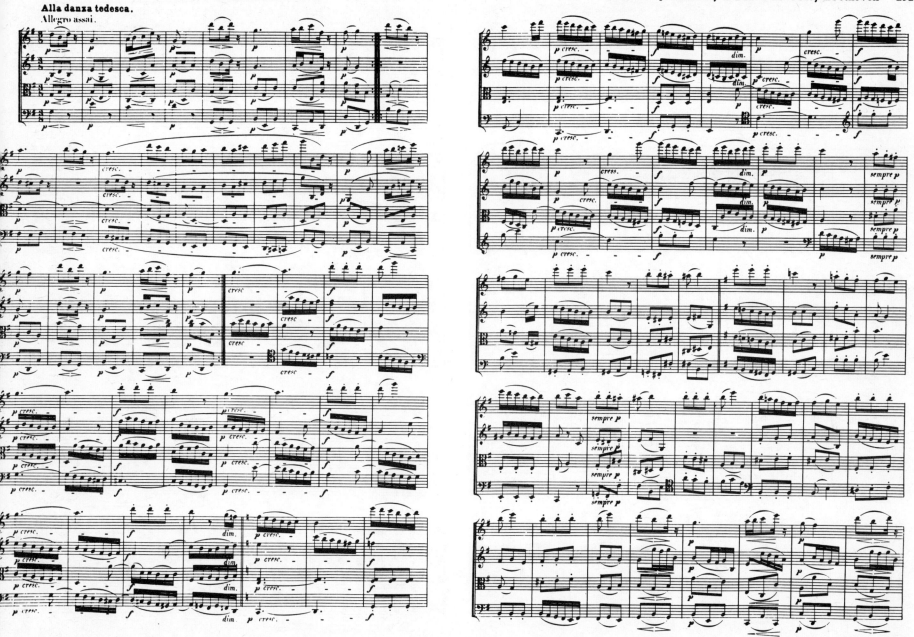

Piano Sonata, F Minor (Appassionata)

Ludwig van Beethoven, 1770-1827 (Opus 57)

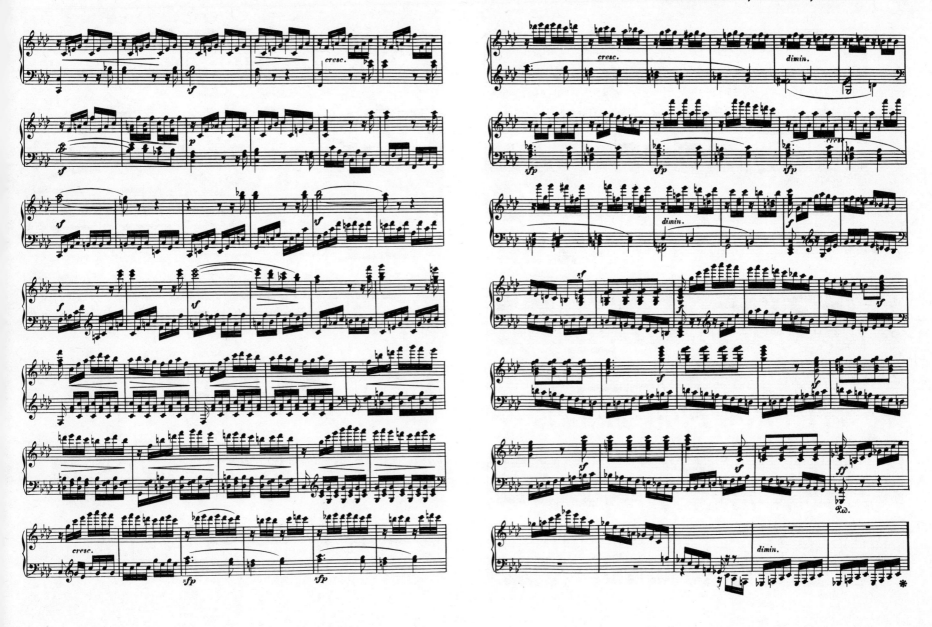

Symphony No. 5, C Minor

Ludwig van Beethoven, 1770–1827 (Opus 67)

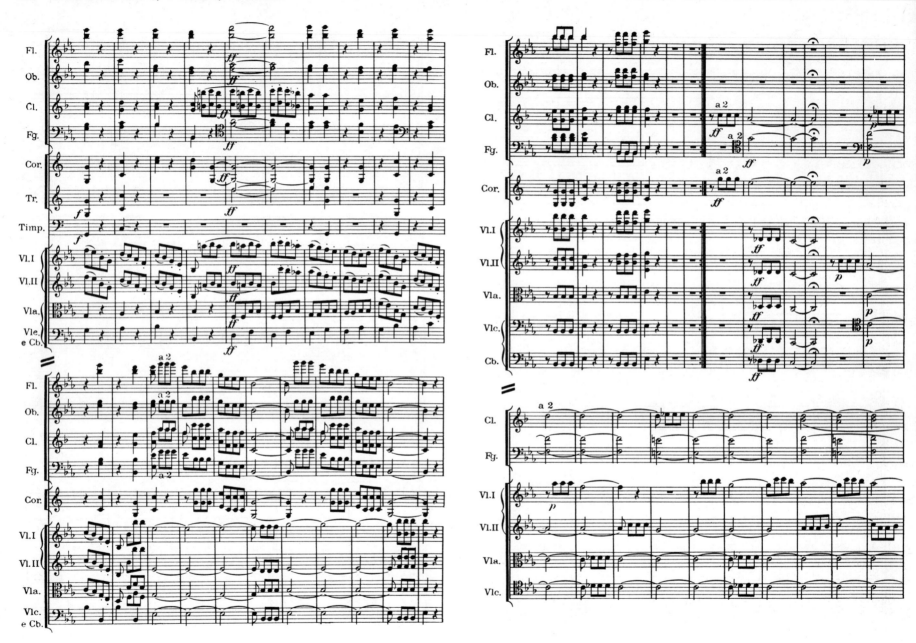

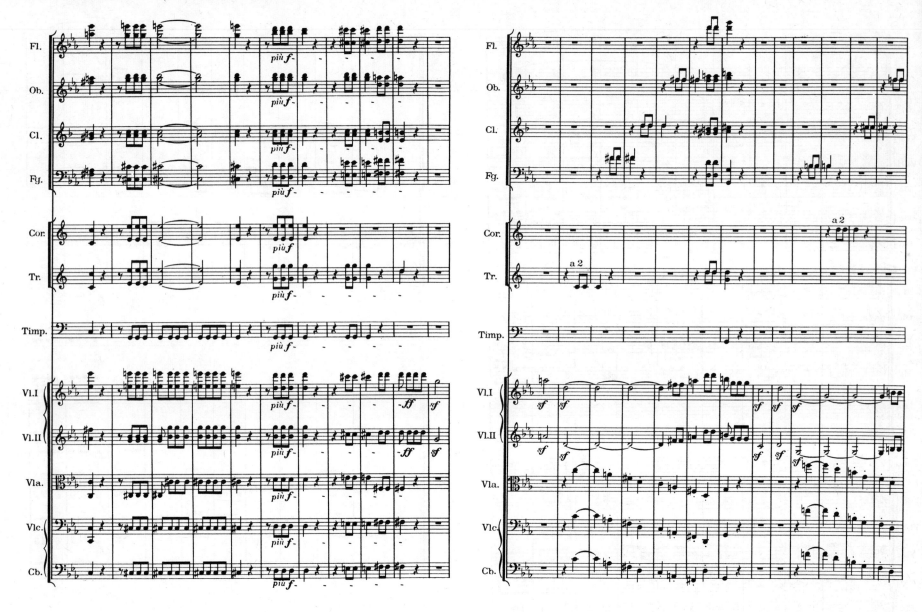

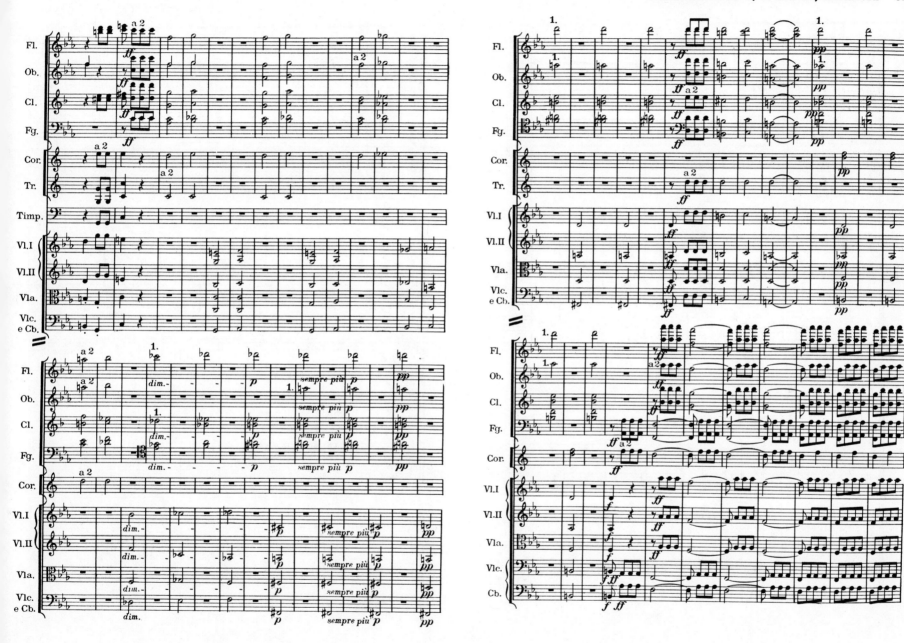

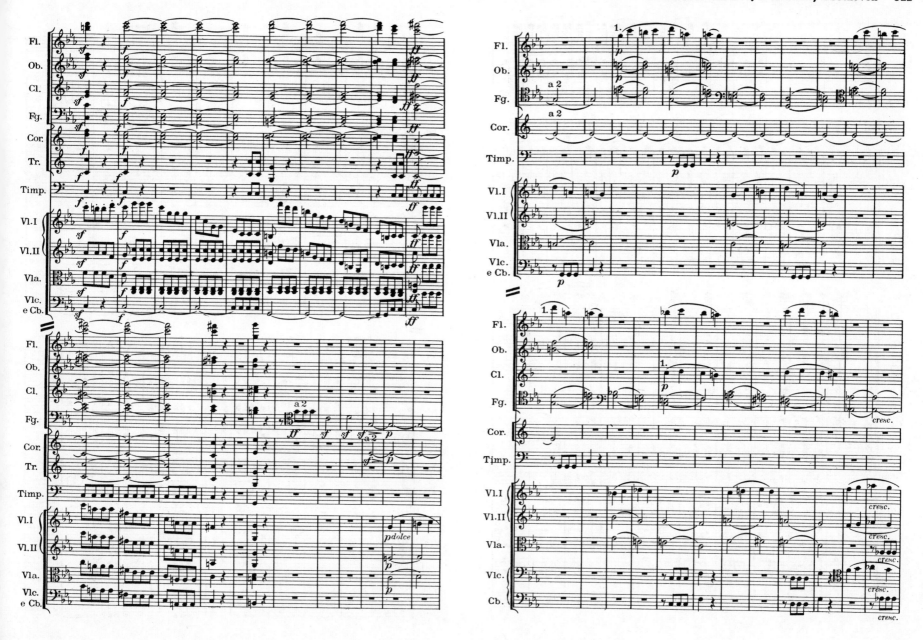

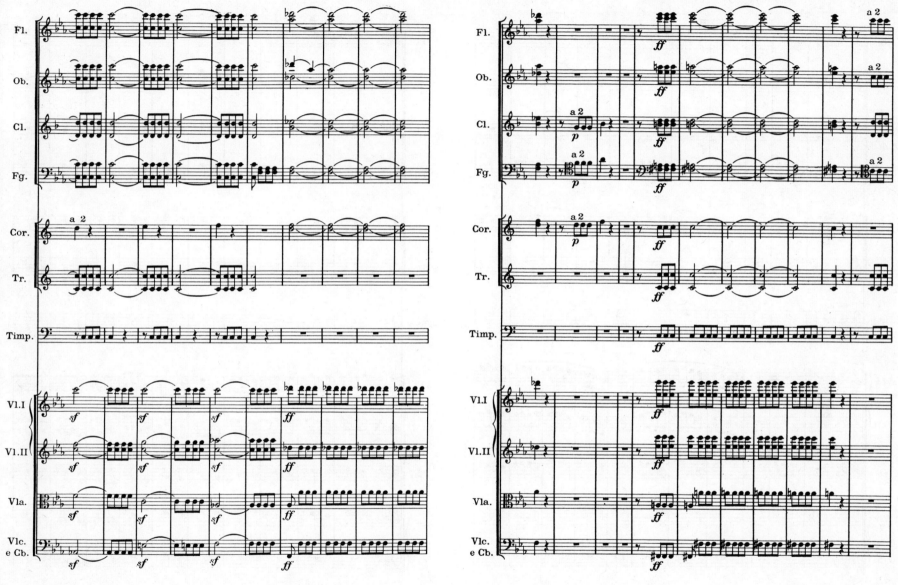

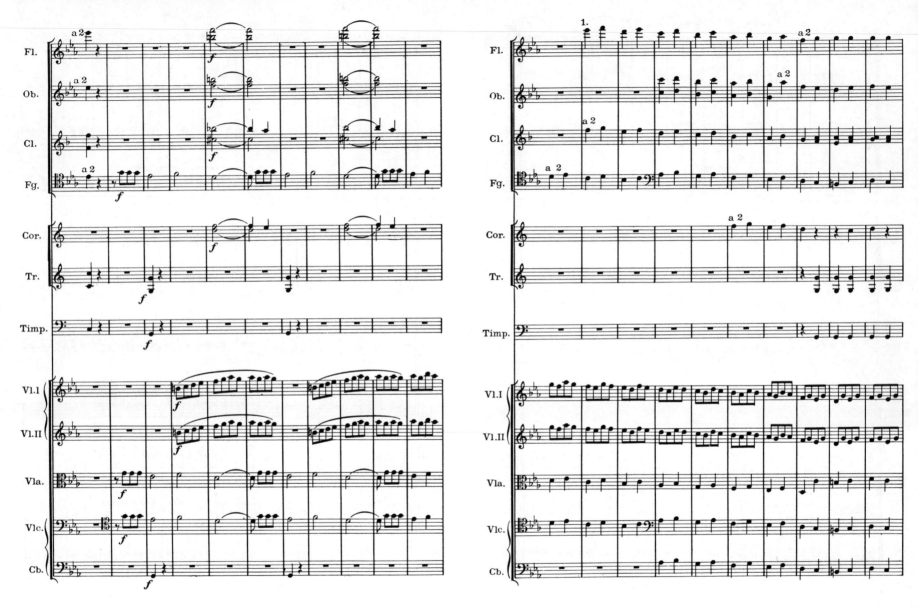

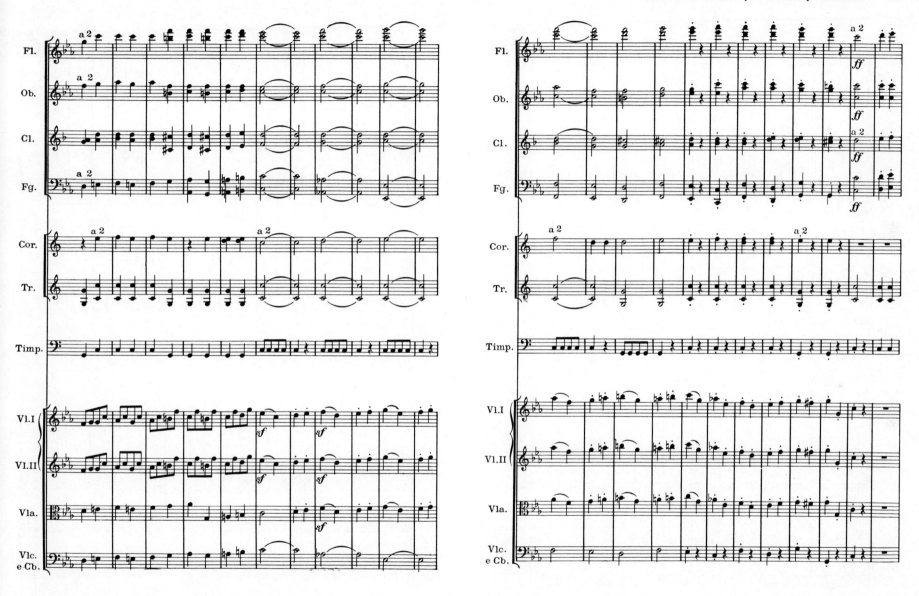

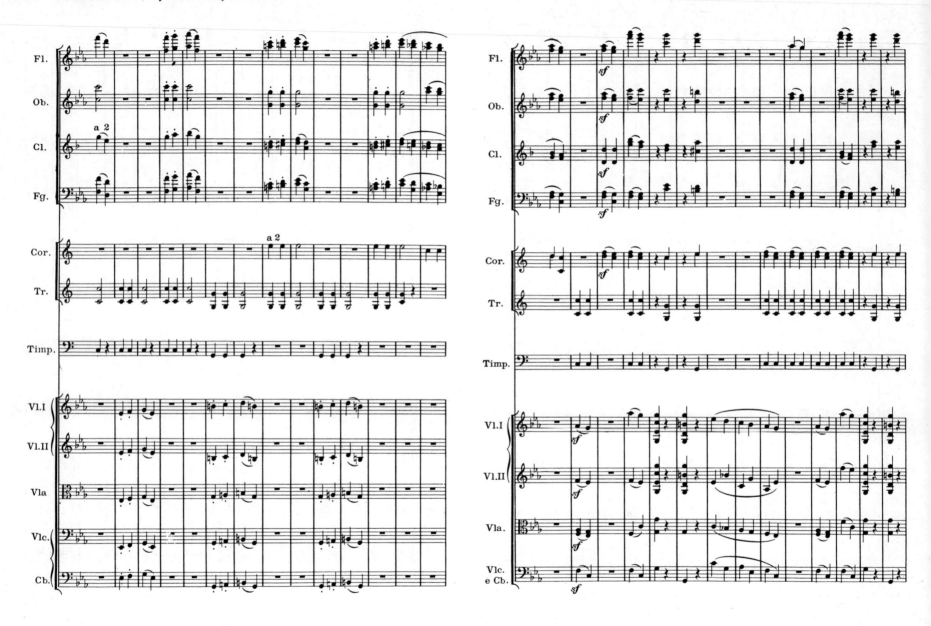

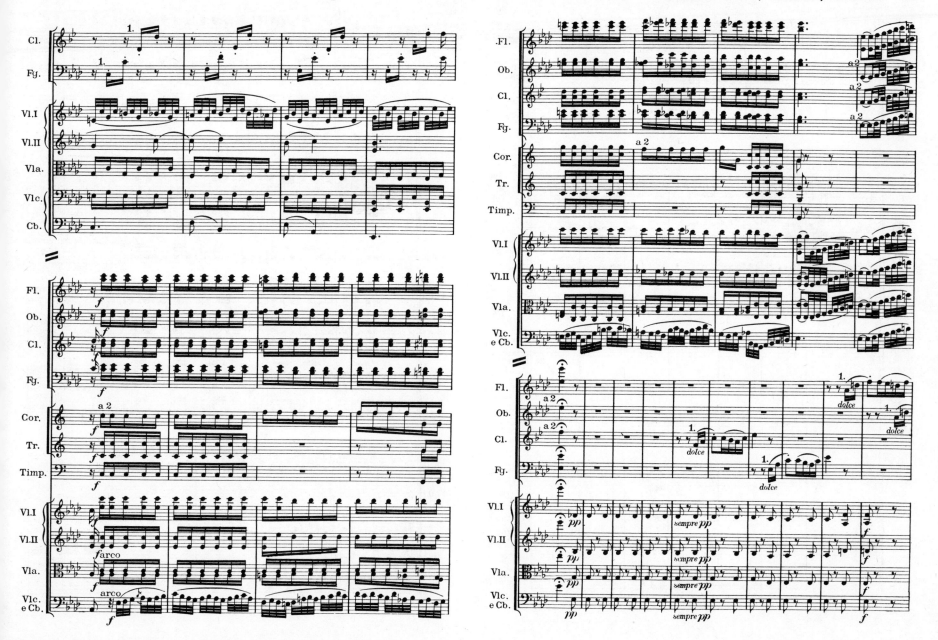

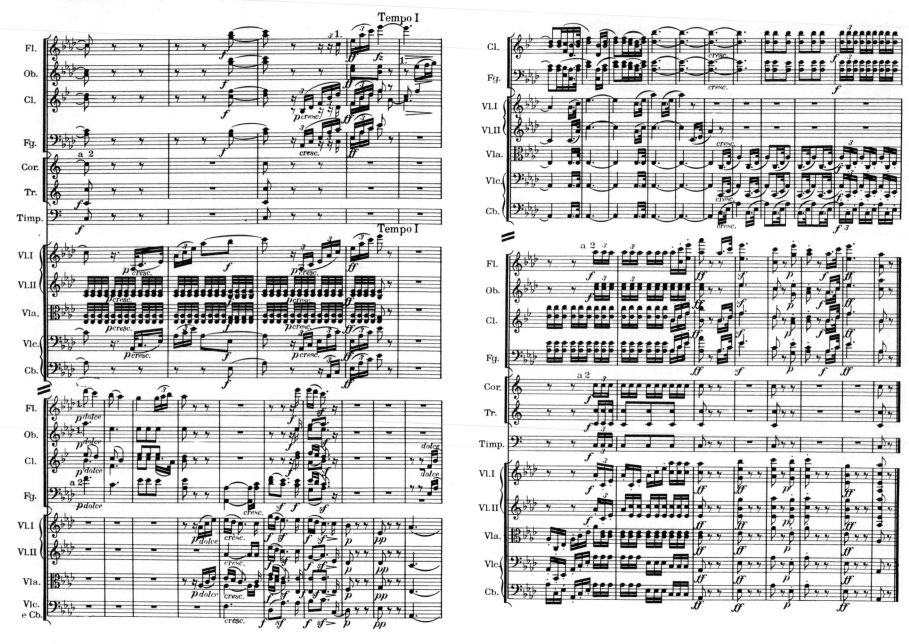

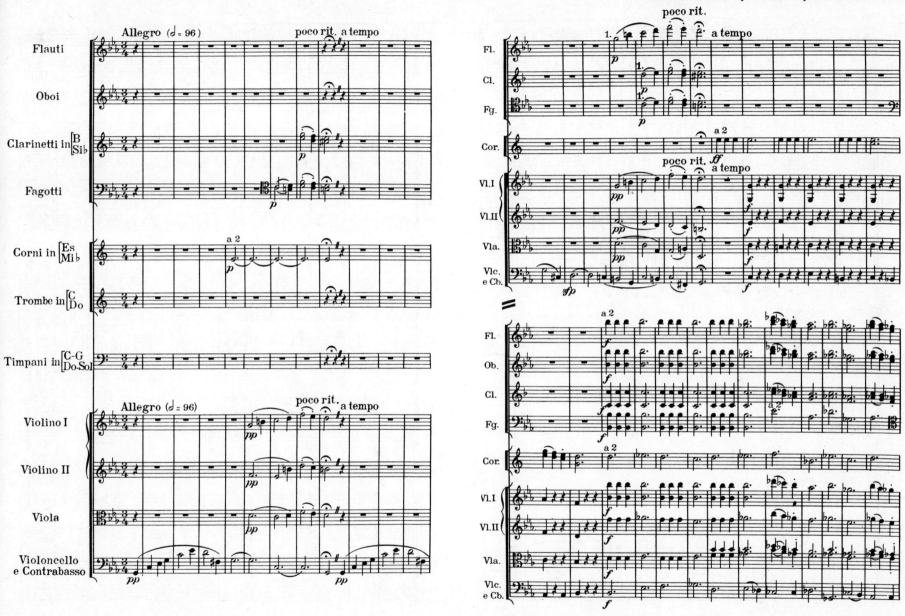

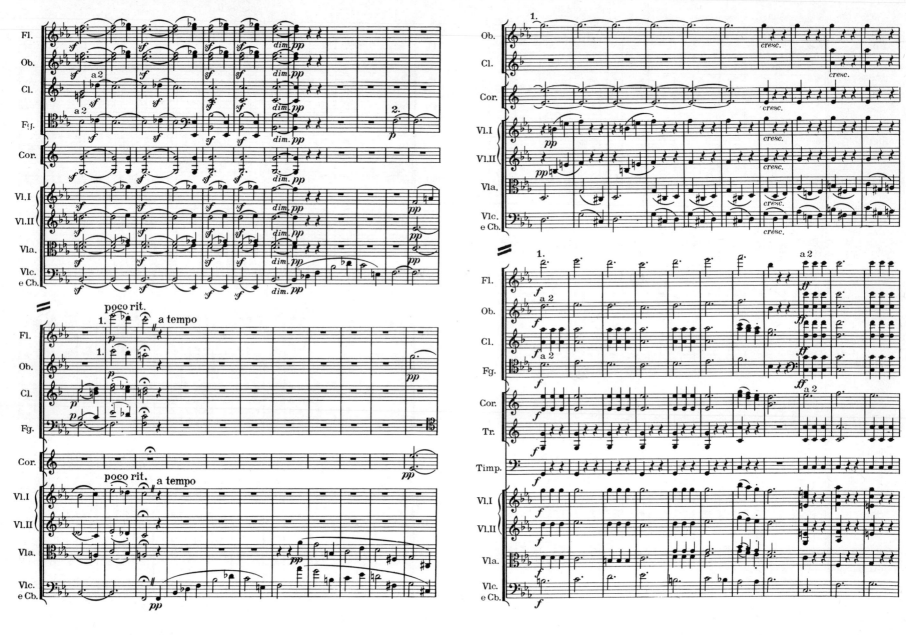

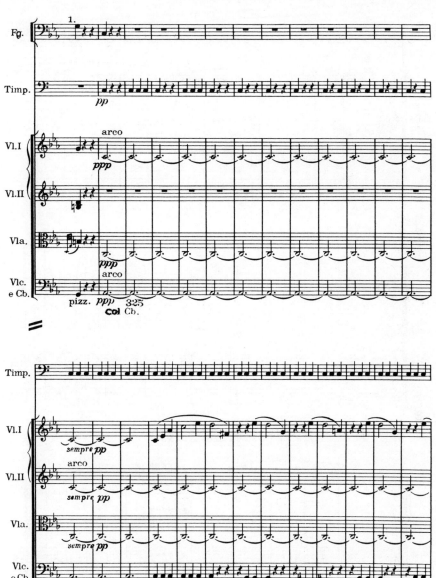

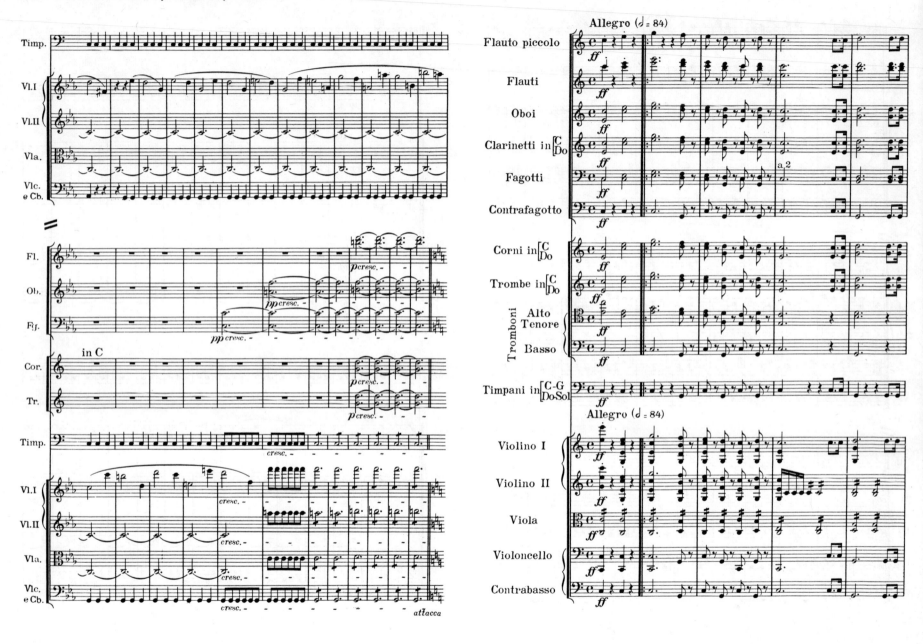

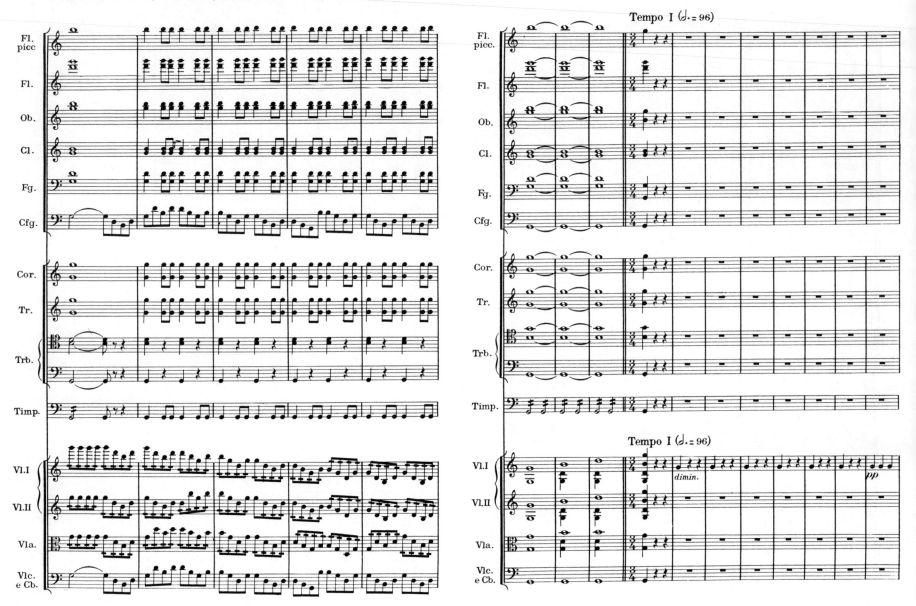

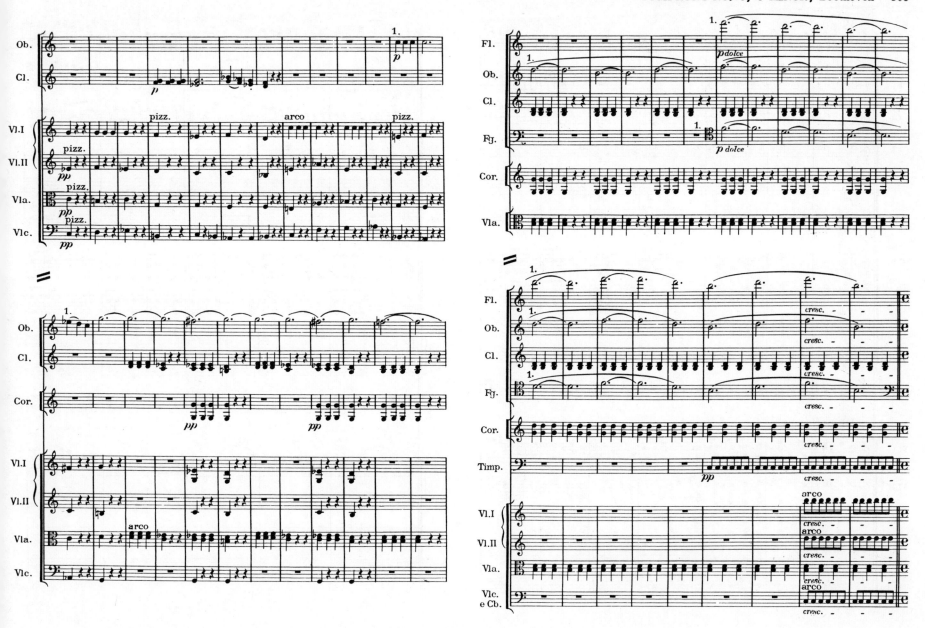

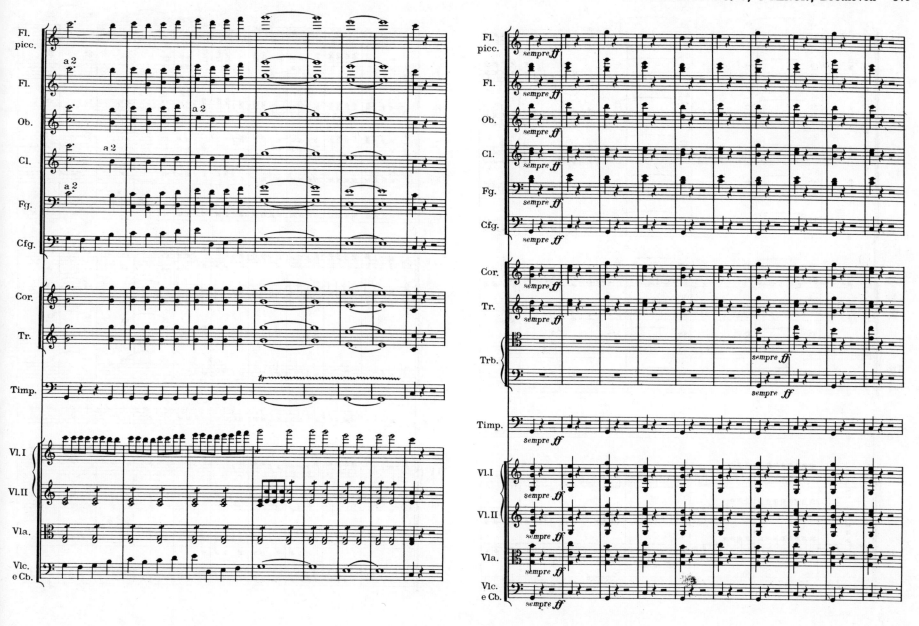

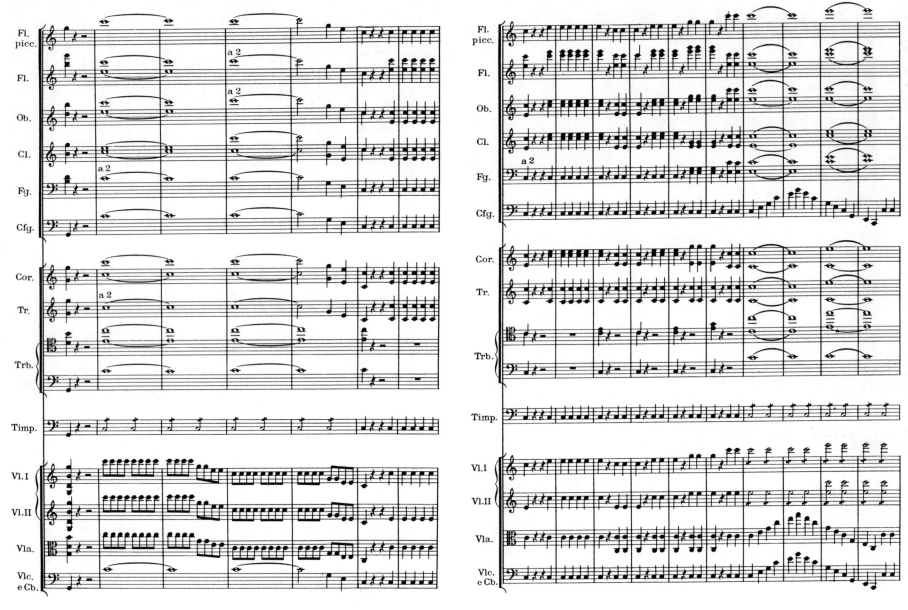

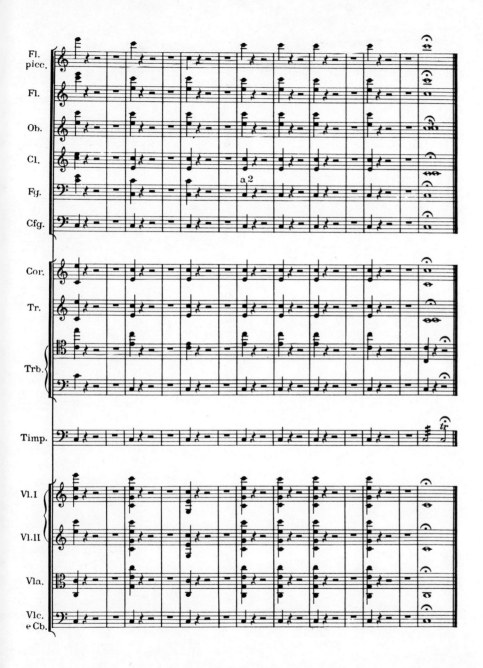

List of Sources and Facsimiles

ZWISCHEN PERG UND TIEFFEM TAL (*p. 33*). *Denkmäler der Tonkunst in Oesterreich*, Jahrg. 14¹.

A CE IOLY MOYS (*p. 35*). Eitner: *Publikationen alterer praktischer und theoretischer Musik*, v. 27.

QUAN DIE VOUS AYME ARDENTEMENT (*p. 36*). Eitner: *Publikationen alterer praktischer und theoretischer Musik*, v. 27.

MORO LASSO (*p. 37*). *Madrigali a cinque voci, Libro sesto.*

LOOK DOWN, O LORD (*p. 39*). *The Collected Works of William Byrd*, v. XI.

PAVAN AND GALLIARD (*p. 41*). *The Fitzwilliam Virginal Book.*

THE SILVER SWAN (*p. 45*). *The Musical Antiquarian Society*, v. 3.

ADORAMUS TE (*p. 47*). *Sämtliche Werke*, Bd. 5.

LAUDA SION (*p. 52*). *Opere Complete*, v. 3; *Sämtliche Werke*, Bd. 5.

MISSA LAUDA SION (*p. 53*). *Opere Complete*, v. 10; *Sämtliche Werke*, Bd. 13.

SONATA PIAN E FORTE (*p. 63*). *Istituzione e monumenti dell' arte musicale italiana*, v. 2.

AMARILLI MIA BELLA (*p. 68*). *Le nuove musiche.*

CRUDA AMARILLI (*p. 69*). *Tutte le opere di Claudio Monteverdi*, Tomo V.

ORFEO, POSSENTE SPIRTO (*p. 72*). *Tutte le opere di Claudio Monteverdi*, Tomo XI.

IL POMO D'ORO (*p. 81*). *Denkmäler der Tonkunst in Oesterreich*, Jahrg. 3ⁱⁱ.

JEPHTE, RECITATIVE AND FINAL CHORUS (*p. 85*). *Carrissimis Werke*, I Abt.

ATTILIA REGOLO, SINFONIA (*p. 90*). Manuscript in Library of Congress.

SONATA, A MAJOR, LONGO 491 (*p. 92*). *Opere complete per il cembalo*, v. 10.

SYMPHONIAE SACRAE NO. X (*p. 95*). *Sämtliche Werke*, Bd. 5.

CHROMATIC FANTASIA (*p. 98*). *Werken van Jan Pieterszn Sweelinck*, v. 1.

FIORI MUSICALI, RICERAR DOPO IL CREDO (*p. 100*). *Fiori Musicali.*

EXCERPT FROM DIDO AND AENEAS (*p. 102*). *Complete works*, v. 3. *Musical Antiquarian Society*, v. 4.

IN DULCI JUBILO (*p. 104*). *Ausgewählte Orgelwerke*, Bd. II.

CONCERTO, C MINOR (*p. 105*). *Les Ouvres de Arcangelo Corelli*, v. 4.

LES TOURBILLONS (*p. 115*). *Ouvres Completes*, v. 1.

L'AUGUSTE FROM PREMIERE ORDRE (*p. 116*). *Pieces de Clavecin*, Livre 1.

The remaining titles may be found in complete works and other readily accessible sources.

Index of Composers

Index of Titles and Subjects